Test Bank

for Serway and Jewett's

Physics
for Scientists and Engineers
Sixth Edition

Volume One

Edward Adelson
Ohio State University

THOMSON
BROOKS/COLE

Australia • Canada • Mexico • Singapore • Spain • United Kingdom • United States

Printed in the United States of America
1 2 3 4 5 6 7 07 06 05 04 03

Printer: Globus Printing

0-534-40954-7

For more information about our products,
contact us at:
Thomson Learning Academic Resource Center
1-800-423-0563

For permission to use material from this text,
contact us by:
Phone: 1-800-730-2214
Fax: 1-800-731-2215
Web: http://www.thomsonrights.com

Asia
Thomson Learning
5 Shenton Way #01-01
UIC Building
Singapore 068808

Australia/New Zealand
Thomson Learning
102 Dodds Street
Southbank, Victoria 3006
Australia

Canada
Nelson
1120 Birchmount Road
Toronto, Ontario M1K 5G4
Canada

Europe/Middle East/South Africa
Thomson Learning
High Holborn House
50/51 Bedford Row
London WC1R 4LR
United Kingdom

Latin America
Thomson Learning
Seneca, 53
Colonia Polanco
11560 Mexico D.F.
Mexico

Spain/Portugal
Paraninfo
Calle/Magallanes, 25
28015 Madrid, Spain

Contents

Preface

In this edition of this test bank, intended to supplement the problems in Serway and Jewett's *Physics for Scientists and Engineers with Modern Physics,* Sixth Edition, the number of qualitative and conceptual multiple-choice questions has been expanded in order to offer a greater array of questions of these types. While many of the questions from the previous edition have been carried over to the new edition, as much as 20 percent of the material is new in the sixth edition. These test questions are also available in electronic form through Brooks/Cole Assessment test-generating software. To obtain a copy of this electronic version, please contact your Thomson Learning Sales Representative. Algorithmic variations on selected problems from this test bank are available for student practice on the Brooks/Cole web site at http://www.pse6.com.

These problems have been carefully checked for accuracy and clarity, many being rewritten for these purposes. For those who might prefer the original versions, a number have been left as originally written. This test bank could not have reached its current improved state without the assistance of Dr. Edwin Lo, for whose many valuable suggestions and ability to ferret out errors I am truly grateful, the technical skills of Martin Arthur, or the encouragement and backup provided by our editor, Rebecca Heider.

Brooks/Cole Publishing and Raymond A. Serway and John W. Jewett gratefully acknowledge the work of the following people who originally prepared and edited the first four editions of these test questions:

Louis H. Caldwell, Providence College
Steven Van Wyck, Olympic College
Michael Carchidi, The Georgia Institute of Technology Physics Department

Dr. Edward Adelson

Physics Department
The Ohio State University
174 West Eighteenth Avenue
Columbus, Ohio 43210
adelson@mps.ohio-state.edu
614-292-2067
614-292-7557 FAX

Chapter 1

Physics and Measurement

Multiple Choice

1. Which of the following products of ratios gives the conversion factor to convert miles per hour $\left(\dfrac{mi}{h}\right)$ to meters per second $\left(\dfrac{m}{s}\right)$?

   a. $\dfrac{5280\ f}{mi} \cdot \dfrac{12\ in}{f} \cdot \dfrac{1\ in}{2.54\ cm} \cdot \dfrac{1\ m}{100\ cm} \cdot \dfrac{1\ h}{3600\ s}$

   b. $\dfrac{5280\ f}{mi} \cdot \dfrac{12\ in}{f} \cdot \dfrac{2.54\ cm}{1\ in} \cdot \dfrac{100\ cm}{1\ m} \cdot \dfrac{1\ h}{3600\ s}$

   c. $\dfrac{1\ mi}{5280\ f} \cdot \dfrac{1\ f}{12\ in} \cdot \dfrac{1\ in}{2.54\ cm} \cdot \dfrac{100\ cm}{1\ m} \cdot \dfrac{3600\ s}{1\ h}$

   d. $\dfrac{5280\ f}{mi} \cdot \dfrac{12\ in}{f} \cdot \dfrac{2.54\ cm}{1\ in} \cdot \dfrac{1\ m}{100\ cm} \cdot \dfrac{1\ h}{3600\ s}$

   e. $\dfrac{5280\ f}{mi} \cdot \dfrac{12\ in}{f} \cdot \dfrac{2.54\ cm}{1\ in} \cdot \dfrac{1\ m}{100\ cm} \cdot \dfrac{3600\ s}{1\ h}$

2. The density of an object is defined as:

   a. the volume occupied by each unit of mass.
   b. the amount of mass for each unit of volume.
   c. the weight of each unit of volume.
   d. the amount of the substance that has unit volume and unit mass.
   e. the amount of the substance that contains as many particles as 12 grams of the carbon-12 isotope.

3. If you drove day and night without stopping for one year without exceeding the legal highway speed limit in the United States, the maximum number of miles you could drive would be closest to:

   a. 8700.
   b. 300 000.
   c. 500 000.
   d. 1 000 000.
   e. 32 000 000.

4.   The term $\frac{1}{2}\rho v^2$ occurs in Bernoulli's equation in Chapter 15, with ρ being the density of a fluid and v its speed. The dimensions of this term are

   a. $M^{-1}L^5T^2$
   b. MLT^2
   c. $ML^{-1}T^{-2}$
   d. $M^{-1}L^9T^{-2}$
   e. $M^{-1}L^3T^{-2}$

5.   Which of the following quantities has the same dimensions as kinetic energy, $\frac{1}{2}mv^2$?

   Note: $[a] = [g] = LT^{-2}$; $[h] = L$ and $[v] = LT^{-1}$.

   a. ma
   b. mvx
   c. mvt
   d. mgh
   e. mgt

6.   The quantity with the same units as force times time, Ft, with dimensions MLT^{-1} is

   a. mv
   b. mvr
   c. mv^2r
   d. ma
   e. $\dfrac{mv^2}{r}$

7.   The equation for the change of position of a train starting at $x = 0$ m is given by $x = \frac{1}{2}at^2 + bt^3$. The dimensions of b are

   a. T^{-3}
   b. LT^{-3}
   c. LT^{-2}
   d. LT^{-1}
   e. $L^{-1}T^{-1}$

8.   One mole of the carbon-12 isotope contains 6.022×10^{23} atoms. What volume in m^3 would be needed to store one mole of cube-shaped children's blocks 2.00 cm long on each side?

    a. 4.8×10^{18}
    b. 1.2×10^{22}
    c. 6.0×10^{23}
    d. 1.2×10^{24}
    e. 4.8×10^{24}

9.   Which of the following products of ratios gives the conversion factors to convert meters per second $\left(\dfrac{m}{s} \right)$ to miles per hour $\left(\dfrac{mi}{h} \right)$?

    a. $\dfrac{5280\ f}{mi} \cdot \dfrac{12\ in}{f} \cdot \dfrac{2.54\ cm}{1\ in} \cdot \dfrac{100\ cm}{1\ m} \cdot \dfrac{3600\ s}{1\ h}$

    b. $\dfrac{5280\ f}{mi} \cdot \dfrac{12\ in}{f} \cdot \dfrac{1\ in}{2.54\ cm} \cdot \dfrac{1\ m}{100\ cm} \cdot \dfrac{1\ h}{3600\ s}$

    c. $\dfrac{5280\ f}{mi} \cdot \dfrac{12\ in}{f} \cdot \dfrac{2.54\ cm}{1\ in} \cdot \dfrac{100\ cm}{1\ m} \cdot \dfrac{1\ h}{3600\ s}$

    d. $\dfrac{1\ mi}{5280\ f} \cdot \dfrac{1\ f}{12\ in} \cdot \dfrac{1\ in}{2.54\ cm} \cdot \dfrac{100\ cm}{1\ m} \cdot \dfrac{3600\ s}{1\ h}$

    e. $\dfrac{1\ mi}{5280\ f} \cdot \dfrac{1\ f}{12\ in} \cdot \dfrac{1\ in}{2.54\ cm} \cdot \dfrac{1\ m}{100\ cm} \cdot \dfrac{3600\ s}{1\ h}$

10.   One U.S. fluid gallon contains a volume of 231 cubic inches. How many liters of gasoline would you have to buy in Canada to fill a 14 gallon tank? (Note: $1\,L = 10^{+3}\ cm^3$.)

    a.   53
    b.   21
    c.   14
    d.   8
    e.   4

Open-Ended Problems

11.   The standard kilogram is a platinum-iridium cylinder 39 mm in height and 39 mm in diameter. What is the density of the material?

12.   A 2.00 m by 3.00 m plate of aluminum has a mass of 324 kg. What is the thickness of the plate? (The density of aluminum is $2.70 \times 10^3\ kg/m^3$.)

13.   What is the mass of air in a room that measures $5.0\ m \times 8.0\ m \times 3.0\ m$? (The density of air is $1/800$ that of water).

14.   The basic function of a carburetor of an automobile is to atomize the gasoline and mix it with air to promote rapid combustion. As an example, assume that 30 cm^3 of gasoline is atomized into N spherical droplets, each with a radius of 2.0×10^{-5} m. What is the total surface area of these N spherical droplets?

Chapter 1

Physics and Measurement

1.   d

2.   b

3.   c

4.   c

5.   d

6.   a

7.   b

8.   a

9.   d

10. a

11. 21 475 kg/m^3

12. 2.00 cm

13. 150 kg

14. 45 000 cm^2

Chapter 2

Motion in One Dimension

Multiple Choice

1. The position of a particle moving along the x axis is given by
    $x = (21 + 22t - 6.0t^2)$ m , where t is in s. What is the average velocity during the
    time interval $t = 1.0$ s to $t = 3.0$ s?

    a. −6.0 m/s
    b. −4.0 m/s
    c. −2.0 m/s
    d. −8.0 m/s
    e. 8.0 m/s

2. A bullet is fired through a board, 14.0 cm thick, with its line of motion
    perpendicular to the face of the board. If it enters with a speed of 450 m/s and
    emerges with a speed of 220 m/s, what is the bullet's acceleration as it passes
    through the board?

    a. −500 km/s^2
    b. −550 km/s^2
    c. −360 km/s^2
    d. −520 km/s^2
    e. −275 km/s^2

3. The position of a particle moving along the x axis is given by $x = 6.0t^2 - 1.0t^3$,
    where x is in meters and t in seconds. What is the position of the particle when it
    achieves its maximum speed in the positive x direction?

    a. 24 m
    b. 12 m
    c. 32 m
    d. 16 m
    e. 2.0 m

4. The velocity of a particle moving along the x axis is given for $t > 0$ by
    $v_x = (32.0t - 2.00t^3)$ m/s, where t is in s. What is the acceleration of the particle
    when (after $t = 0$) it achieves its maximum displacement in the positive x
    direction?

    a. −64.0 m/s^2
    b. zero
    c. 128 m/s^2
    d. 32.0 m/s^2
    e. −32.0 m/s^2

5.   The position of a particle as it moves along the x axis is given for $t > 0$ by $x = \left(t^3 - 3t^2 + 6t\right)$ m, where t is in s. Where is the particle when it achieves its minimum speed (after $t = 0$)?

   a.   3 m
   b.   4 m
   c.   8 m
   d.   2 m
   e.   7 m

6.   The position of a particle as it moves along the x axis is given by $x = 15e^{-2t}$ m, where t is in s. What is the acceleration of the particle at $t = 1$ s?

   a.   22 m/s
   b.   60 m/s
   c.   8.1 m/s
   d.   15 m/s
   e.   35 m/s

7. V_x is the velocity of a particle moving along the x axis as shown. If $x = 2.0$ m at $t = 1.0$ s, what is the position of the particle at $t = 6.0$ s?

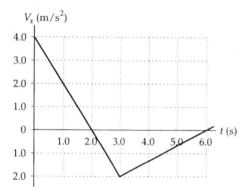

   a.   −2.0 m
   b.   +2.0 m
   c.   +1.0 m
   d.   −1.0 m
   e.   6.0 m

8.   A particle moving along the x axis has a position given by $x = \left(24t - 2.0t^3\right)$ m, where t is measured in s. What is the magnitude of the acceleration of the particle at the instant when its velocity is zero?

   a.   24 m/s^2
   b.   zero
   c.   12 m/s^2
   d.   48 m/s^2
   e.   36 m/s^2

9.   At $t = 0$, a particle is located at $x = 25$ m and has a velocity of 15 m/s in the positive x direction. The acceleration of the particle varies with time as shown in the diagram. What is the velocity of the particle at $t = 5.0$ s?

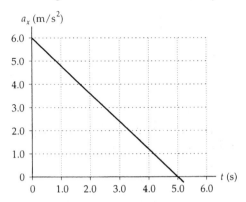

a.   +15 m/s
b.   −15 m/s
c.   +30 m/s
d.   0
e.   −1.2 m/s

10.   At $t = 0$, a particle is located at $x = 25$ m and has a velocity of 15 m/s in the positive x direction. The acceleration of the particle varies with time as shown in the diagram. What is the position of the particle at $t = 5.0$ s?

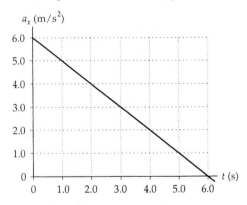

a.   175 m
b.   125 m
c.   138 m
d.   154 m
e.   165 m

11.   A particle confined to motion along the x axis moves with constant acceleration from $x = 2.0$ m to $x = 8.0$ m during a 2.5-s time interval. The velocity of the particle at $x = 8.0$ m is 2.8 m/s. What is the acceleration during this time interval?

    a. 0.48 m/s^2
    b. 0.32 m/s^2
    c. 0.64 m/s^2
    d. 0.80 m/s^2
    e. 0.57 m/s^2

12.   A proton moving along the x axis has an initial velocity of 4.0×10^6 m/s and a constant acceleration of 6.0×10^{12} m/s^2. What is the velocity of the proton after it has traveled a distance of 80 cm?

    a. 5.1×10^6 m/s
    b. 6.3×10^6 m/s
    c. 4.8×10^6 m/s
    d. 3.9×10^6 m/s
    e. 2.9×10^6 m/s

13.   A particle moving with a constant acceleration has a velocity of 20 cm/s when its position is $x = 10$ cm. Its position 7.0 s later is $x = -30$ cm. What is the acceleration of the particle?

    a. -7.3 cm/s^2
    b. -8.9 cm/s^2
    c. -11 cm/s^2
    d. -15 cm/s^2
    e. -13 cm/s^2

14.   An automobile moving along a straight track changes its velocity from 40 m/s to 80 m/s in a distance of 200 m. What is the (constant) acceleration of the vehicle during this time?

    a. 8.0 m/s
    b. 9.6 m/s
    c. 12 m/s
    d. 6.9 m/s
    e. 0.20 m/s

15.   In 2.0 s, a particle moving with constant acceleration along the x axis goes from $x = 10$ m to $x = 50$ m. The velocity at the end of this time interval is 10 m/s. What is the acceleration of the particle?

    a. $+15$ m/s^2
    b. $+20$ m/s^2
    c. -20 m/s^2
    d. -10 m/s^2
    e. -15 m/s^2

16. An automobile manufacturer claims that its product will, starting from rest, travel 0.40 km in 9.0 s. What is the magnitude of the constant acceleration required to do this?

    a. 9.9 m/s^2
    b. 8.9 m/s^2
    c. 6.6 m/s^2
    d. 5.6 m/s^2
    e. 4.6 m/s^2

17. An automobile traveling along a straight road increases its speed from 30.0 m/s to 50.0 m/s in a distance of 180 m. If the acceleration is constant, how much time elapses while the auto moves this distance?

    a. 6.00 s
    b. 4.50 s
    c. 3.60 s
    d. 4.00 s
    e. 9.00 s

18. An object moving on the x axis with a constant acceleration increases its x coordinate by 80 m in a time of 5.0 s and has a velocity of +20 m/s at the end of this time. Determine the acceleration of the object during this motion.

    a. -1.6 m/s^2
    b. $+6.4 \text{ m/s}^2$
    c. $+1.6 \text{ m/s}^2$
    d. -2.0 m/s^2
    e. -6.4 m/s^2

19. An electron, starting from rest and moving with a constant acceleration, travels 2.0 cm in 5.0 ms. What is the magnitude of this acceleration?

    a. 2.5 km/s^2
    b. 0.80 km/s^2
    c. 1.6 km/s^2
    d. 1.3 km/s^2
    e. 3.2 km/s^2

20. A particle starts from rest at $x = 0$ and moves for 10 s with an acceleration of $+2.0 \text{ cm/s}^2$. For the next 20 s, the acceleration of the particle is -1.0 cm/s^2. What is the position of the particle at the end of this motion?

    a. zero
    b. +3.0 m
    c. −1.0 m
    d. +2.0 m
    e. −3.0 m

21.   A rocket, initially at rest, is fired vertically with an upward acceleration of 10 m/s². At an altitude of 0.50 km, the engine of the rocket cuts off. What is the maximum altitude it achieves?

   a.   1.9 km
   b.   1.3 km
   c.   1.6 km
   d.   1.0 km
   e.   2.1 km

22.   A ball is thrown vertically upward with an initial speed of 20 m/s. Two seconds later, a stone is thrown vertically (from the same initial height as the ball) with an initial speed of 24 m/s. At what height above the release point will the ball and stone pass each other?

   a.   17 m
   b.   21 m
   c.   18 m
   d.   27 m
   e.   31 m

23.   An object is thrown vertically and has an upward velocity of 18 m/s when it reaches one fourth of its maximum height above its launch point. What is the initial (launch) speed of the object?

   a.   35 m/s
   b.   25 m/s
   c.   30 m/s
   d.   21 m/s
   e.   17 m/s

24.   A stone is thrown from the top of a building with an initial velocity of 20 m/s downward. The top of the building is 60 m above the ground. How much time elapses between the instant of release and the instant of impact with the ground?

   a.   2.0 s
   b.   6.1 s
   c.   3.5 s
   d.   1.6 s
   e.   1.0 s

25.   An object is thrown downward with an initial ($t = 0$) speed of 10 m/s from a height of 60 m above the ground. At the same instant ($t = 0$), a second object is propelled vertically upward from ground level with a speed of 40 m/s. At what height above the ground will the two objects pass each other?

   a.   53 m
   b.   41 m
   c.   57 m
   d.   46 m
   e.   37 m

26.   A toy rocket, launched from the ground, rises vertically with an acceleration of 20 m/s² for 6.0 s until its motor stops. Disregarding any air resistance, what maximum height above the ground will the rocket achieve?

    a.   1.1 km
    b.   0.73 km
    c.   1.9 km
    d.   0.39 km
    e.   1.5 km

27.   A rock is thrown downward from an unknown height above the ground with an initial speed of 10 m/s. It strikes the ground 3.0 s later. Determine the initial height of the rock above the ground.

    a.   44 m
    b.   14 m
    c.   74 m
    d.   30 m
    e.   60 m

28.   A ball thrown vertically from ground level is caught 3.0 s later by a person on a balcony which is 14 m above the ground. Determine the initial speed of the ball.

    a.   19 m/s
    b.   4.7 m/s
    c.   10 m/s
    d.   34 m/s
    e.   17 m/s

29.   An object is thrown vertically upward such that it has a speed of 25 m/s when it reaches two thirds of its maximum height above the launch point. Determine this maximum height.

    a.   64 m
    b.   48 m
    c.   32 m
    d.   96 m
    e.   75 m

30.   The velocity at the midway point of a ball able to reach a height y when thrown with velocity v_0 at the origin is:

    a. $\dfrac{v_0}{2}$

    b. $\sqrt{v_0^2 2gy}$

    c. $\sqrt{\dfrac{v_0^2}{2}}$

    d. $\sqrt{v_0^2 + 2gy}$

    e. gy

31.   When Jim and Rob ride bicycles, Jim can only accelerate at three quarters the acceleration of Rob. Both start from rest at the bottom of a long straight road with constant upward slope. If Rob takes 5.0 minutes to reach the top, how much earlier should Jim start to reach the top at the same time as Rob?

   a.   25 s
   b.   40 s
   c.   46 s
   d.   55 s
   e.   75 s

32.   When starting from rest at the bottom of a straight road with constant upward slope, Joan bicycles to the top 50.0 s ahead of Sally, whose travel time is 5.00 minutes. What is the ratio of Joan's acceleration to Sally's acceleration?

   a.   0.694
   b.   0.833
   c.   1.20
   d.   1.44
   e.   6.0

33.   To help Kim practice for the Special Olympics, Sally runs beside him for half the required distance. She runs the remaining distance at her regular speed and arrives 90 seconds ahead of Kim. What is the ratio of Sally's regular speed to Kim's speed? Use t_{Kim} for Kim's total time.

   a. $\dfrac{t_{Kim}}{90 \text{ s}}$

   b. $\dfrac{t_{Kim}}{t_{Kim} - 90 \text{ s}}$

   c. $\dfrac{t_{Kim}}{t_{Kim} - 180 \text{ s}}$

   d. $\dfrac{t_{Kim}}{180 \text{ s}}$

   e. $\dfrac{t_{Kim} - 90 \text{ s}}{t_{Kim} - 180 \text{ s}}$

34.   The position of a particle moving along the y-axis has a position given by $y = 0.20 \text{ m} + \left(8.0\dfrac{\text{m}}{\text{s}}\right)t - \left(10\dfrac{\text{m}}{\text{s}^2}\right)t^2$. Is there any time interval during which the particle is not moving?

   a.   Yes, from 0.60 s to 1.00 s.
   b.   Yes, from 0.795 s to 0.805 s.
   c.   Yes, at the time $t = 0.80 \text{ s}$.
   d.   No, the velocity is never zero.
   e.   No, an instant is not the same as a time interval.

35.   A particle moving along the x-axis has a position given by $x = 54t - 2.0t^3$ m. At the time $t = 3.0$ s, the speed of the particle is zero. Which statement is correct?

    a.   The particle remains at rest after $t = 3.0$ s.
    b.   The particle no longer accelerates after $t = 3.0$ s.
    c.   The particle can be found at positions $x < 0$ m only when $t < 0$ s.
    d.   All of the above are correct.
    e.   None of the above is correct.

36.   Two identical balls are at rest side by side at the bottom of a hill. Some time after ball A is kicked up the hill, ball B is given a kick up the hill. Ball A is headed downhill when it passes ball B headed up the hill. At the instant when ball A passes ball B,

    a.   it has the same position and velocity as ball B.
    b.   it has the same position and acceleration as ball B.
    c.   it has the same velocity and acceleration as ball B.
    d.   it has the same displacement and velocity as ball B.
    e.   it has the same position, displacement and velocity as ball B.

37.   The position of an object at equal time intervals is shown below:

which graph below correctly represents position versus time for this object?

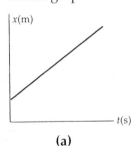

(a)

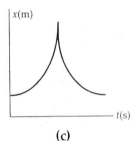

(b)   **(c)**

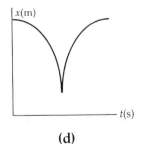

(d)

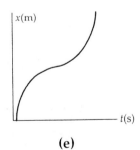

(e)

38.   Two identical balls are at rest and side by side at the top of a hill. You let one ball, A, start rolling down the hill. A little later you start the second ball, B, down the hill by giving it a shove. The second ball rolls down the hill along a line parallel to the path of the first ball and passes it. At the instant ball B passes ball A:

    a.   it has the same position and the same velocity as A.
    b.   it has the same position and the same acceleration as A.
    c.   it has the same velocity and the same acceleration as A.
    d.   it has the same displacement and the same velocity as A.
    e.   it has the same position, displacement and velocity as A.

39.   The graph below shows the velocity versus time graph for a ball. Which explanation best fits the motion of the ball as shown by the graph?

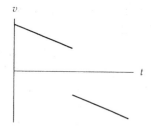

    a.   The ball is falling, is caught, and is thrown down with greater velocity.
    b.   The ball is rolling, stops, and then continues rolling.
    c.   The ball is rising, hits the ceiling, and falls down.
    d.   The ball is falling, hits the floor, and bounces up.
    e.   The ball is rising, is caught, and then is thrown down.

40.   A boy on a skate board skates off a horizontal bench at a velocity of 10 m/s. One tenth of a second after he leaves the bench, to two significant figures, the magnitudes of his velocity and acceleration are:

    a.   10 m/s; 9.8 m/s^2.
    b.   9.0 m/s; 9.8 m/s^2.
    c.   9.0 m/s; 9.0 m/s^2.
    d.   1.0 m/s; 9.0 m/s^2.
    e.   1.0 m/s; 9.8 m/s^2.

41.   Five motion diagrams in which points represent the positions of an object at equal time intervals are shown below. Which statement is correct?

A • • • • •
B • • • • ••
C •• • • • • •
D ••• • • • •••
E • • • • • • • • •

   a.   A has the greatest speed and the greatest acceleration.
   b.   C has decreasing speed.
   c.   D slows down and then speeds up.
   d.   D speeds up and then slows down.
   e.   E has a greater speed than A.

42.   Two children start at one end of a street, the origin, run to the other end, then head back. On the way back Joan is ahead of Mike. Which statement is correct about the distances run and the displacements from the origin?

   a.   Joan has run a greater distance and her displacement is greater than Mike's.
   b.   Mike has run a greater distance and his displacement is greater than Joan's.
   c.   Joan has run a greater distance, but her displacement is less than Mike's.
   d.   Mike has run a greater distance, but his displacement is less than Joan's.
   e.   Mike has run a shorter distance, and his displacement is less than Joan's.

43.   A juggler throws two balls to the same height so that one is at the halfway point going up when the other is at the halfway point coming down. At that point:

   a.   Their velocities and accelerations are equal.
   b.   Their velocities are equal but their accelerations are equal and opposite.
   c.   Their accelerations are equal but their velocities are equal and opposite.
   d.   Their velocities and accelerations are both equal and opposite.
   e.   Their velocities are equal to their accelerations.

44.   A car travels north at 30 m/s for one half hour. It then travels south at 40 m/s for 15 minutes. The total distance the car has traveled and its displacement are:

   a.   18 km; 18 km S.
   b.   36 km; 36 km S.
   c.   36 km; 36 km N.
   d.   90 km; 18 km N.
   e.   90 km; 36 km N.

45.   A skier leaves a ski jump with a horizontal velocity of 29.4 m/s. The instant before she lands three seconds later, the magnitudes of the horizontal and vertical components of her velocity are:

   a.   0; 29.4 m/s.
   b.   29.4 m/s; 0.
   c.   29.4 m/s; 29.4 m/s.
   d.   29.4 m/s; 41.6 m/s.
   e.   41.6 m/s; 41.6 m/s.

Open-Ended Problems

46.   A 50-gram superball traveling at 25 m/s is bounced off a brick wall and rebounds at 22 m/s. A high-speed camera records this event. If the ball is in contact with the wall for 3.5 ms, what is the average acceleration of the ball during this time interval?

47.   A boat moves at 10 m/s relative to the water. If the boat is in a river where the current is 2.0 m/s, how long does it take the boat to make a complete round trip of 1.0 km upstream followed by a 1.0 km trip downstream?

48.   A bicyclist starts down a hill with an initial speed of 2.0 m/s. She moves down the hill with a constant acceleration, arriving at the bottom of the hill with a speed of 8.0 m/s. If the hill is 12 m long, how long did it take the bicyclist to travel down the hill?

49.   A helicopter descends from a height of 600 m with uniform negative acceleration, reaching the ground at rest in 5.00 minutes. Determine the acceleration of the helicopter and its initial downward velocity.

50.   A speedy tortoise can run with a velocity of 10 cm/s and a hare can run 20 times as fast. In a race, they both start at the same time, but the hare stops to rest for 2.0 minutes. The tortoise wins by a shell (20 cm). What was the length of the race?

51.   A peregrine falcon dives at a pigeon. The falcon starts with zero downward velocity and falls with the acceleration of gravity. If the pigeon is 76.0 m below the initial height of the falcon, how long does it take the falcon to intercept the pigeon?

52.   Starting from rest, a car travels 1,350 meters in 1.00 minute. It accelerated at 1.0 m/s^2 until it reached its cruising speed. Then it drove the remaining distance at constant velocity. What was its cruising speed?

53.   A car originally traveling at 30 m/s manages to brake for 5.0 seconds while traveling 125 m downhill. At that point the brakes fail. After an additional 5.0 seconds it travels an additional 150 m down the hill. What was the acceleration of the car after the brakes failed?

Chapter 2

Motion in One Dimension

1.	c	28.	a
2.	b	29.	d
3.	d	30.	c
4.	a	31.	c
5.	b	32.	d
6.	c	33.	c
7.	d	34.	e
8.	a	35.	e
9.	c	36.	b
10.	d	37.	e
11.	b	38.	b
12.	a	39.	c
13.	a	40.	a
14.	c	41.	d
15.	d	42.	c
16.	a	43.	c
17.	b	44.	d
18.	c	45.	c
19.	c	46.	$13{,}430 \text{ m/s}^2$
20.	b	47.	208.3 s
21.	d	48.	2.4 s
22.	a	49.	$-0.0133 \text{ m/s}^2, 4.0 \text{ m/s}$
23.	d	50.	12.62 m
24.	a	51.	3.94 s
25.	b	52.	30 m/s
26.	a	53.	4.0 m/s^2
27.	c		

Chapter 3

Vectors

Multiple Choice

On occasion, the notation $\mathbf{A} = [A, \theta]$ will be a shorthand notation for
$\mathbf{A} = A \cos \theta\, \mathbf{i} + A \sin \theta\, \mathbf{j}$.

1.   If $\mathbf{A} = [15, 80°]$ and $\mathbf{B} = 12\mathbf{i} - 16\mathbf{j}$, what is the magnitude of $\mathbf{A} - \mathbf{B}$?

    a.   15
    b.   35
    c.   32
    d.   5.0
    e.   23

2.   Vectors $\mathbf{A}$ and $\mathbf{B}$ are shown. What is the magnitude of a vector $\mathbf{C}$ if $\mathbf{C} = \mathbf{A} - \mathbf{B}$?

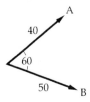

    a.   46
    b.   10
    c.   30
    d.   78
    e.   90

3.   If $\mathbf{A} = 12\mathbf{i} - 16\mathbf{j}$ and $\mathbf{B} = -24\mathbf{i} + 10\mathbf{j}$, what is the magnitude of the vector
    $\mathbf{C} = 2\mathbf{A} - \mathbf{B}$?

    a.   42
    b.   22
    c.   64
    d.   90
    e.   13

4.   If $\mathbf{A} = 12\mathbf{i} - 16\mathbf{j}$ and $\mathbf{B} = -24\mathbf{i} + 10\mathbf{j}$, what is the direction of the vector $\mathbf{C} = 2\mathbf{A} - \mathbf{B}$?

    a.   −49°
    b.   −41°
    c.   −90°
    d.   +49°
    e.   +21°

5.   If **C** = [10 m, 30°] and **D** = [25 m, 130°], what is the magnitude of the sum of these two vectors?

   a.   20 m
   b.   35 m
   c.   15 m
   d.   25 m
   e.   50 m

6.   If **C** = [10 m, 30°] and **D** = [25 m, 130°], what is the direction of the sum of these two vectors?

   a.   17°
   b.   73°
   c.   107°
   d.   163°
   e.   100°

7.   A vector, **B**, when added to the vector **C** = $3\mathbf{i} + 4\mathbf{j}$ yields a resultant vector which is in the positive y direction and has a magnitude equal to that of **C**. What is the magnitude of **B**?

   a.   3.2
   b.   6.3
   c.   9.5
   d.   18
   e.   5

8.   If vector **B** is added to vector **A**, the result is $6\mathbf{i} + \mathbf{j}$. If **B** is subtracted from **A**, the result is $-4\mathbf{i} + 7\mathbf{j}$. What is the magnitude of **A**?

   a.   5.1
   b.   4.1
   c.   5.4
   d.   5.8
   e.   8.2

9.   If **C** = [2.5 cm, 80°], i.e., the magnitude and direction of **C** are 2.5 cm and 80°, **D** = [3.5 cm, 120°], and **E** = **D** – 2**C**, what is the direction of **E** (to the nearest degree)?

   a.   247°
   b.   235°
   c.   243°
   d.   216°
   e.   144°

10.   If vector **C** is added to vector **B**, the result is $-9\mathbf{i} - 8\mathbf{j}$. If **B** is subtracted from **C**, the result is $5\mathbf{i} + 4\mathbf{j}$. What is the direction of **B** (to the nearest degree)?

   a.   225°
   b.   221°
   c.   230°
   d.   236°
   e.   206°

11.   A vector **A** is added to $\mathbf{B} = 6\mathbf{i} - 8\mathbf{j}$. The resultant vector is in the positive x direction and has a magnitude equal to **A**. What is the magnitude of **A**?

   a.   11
   b.   5.1
   c.   7.1
   d.   8.3
   e.   12.2

12.   A vector **A** is added to $\mathbf{B} = 6\mathbf{i} - 8\mathbf{j}$. The resultant vector is in the positive x direction and has a magnitude equal to that of **A**. What is the direction of **A**?

   a.   74°
   b.   100°
   c.   −81°
   d.   −62°
   e.   106°

13.   If two collinear vectors **A** and **B** are added, the resultant has a magnitude equal to 4.0. If **B** is subtracted from **A**, the resultant has a magnitude equal to 8.0. What is the magnitude of **B**?

   a.   2.0
   b.   3.0
   c.   4.0
   d.   5.0
   e.   6.0

14.   If two collinear vectors **A** and **B** are added, the resultant has a magnitude equal to 4.0. If **B** is subtracted from **A**, the resultant has a magnitude equal to 8.0. What is the magnitude of **A**?

   a.   2.0
   b.   3.0
   c.   4.0
   d.   5.0
   e.   6.0

15.   When vector **A** is added to vector **B**, which has a magnitude of 5.0, the vector representing their sum is perpendicular to **A** and has a magnitude that is twice that of **A**. What is the magnitude of **A**?

    a.   2.2
    b.   2.5
    c.   4.5
    d.   5.0
    e.   7.0

16.   Starting from one oasis, a camel walks 25 km in a direction 30° south of west and then walks 30 km toward the north to a second oasis. What distance separates the two oases?

    a.   15 km
    b.   48 km
    c.   28 km
    d.   53 km
    e.   55 km

17.   Starting from one oasis, a camel walks 25 km in a direction 30° south of west and then walks 30 km toward the north to a second oasis. What is the direction from the first oasis to the second oasis?

    a.   21° N of W
    b.   39° W of N
    c.   69° N of W
    d.   51° W of N
    e.   42° W of N

18.   The three forces shown act on a particle. What is the magnitude of the resultant of these three forces?

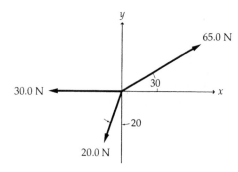

    a.   27.0 N
    b.   33.2 N
    c.   36.3 N
    d.   23.8 N
    e.   105 N

19. The three forces shown act on a particle. What is the direction of the resultant of these three forces?

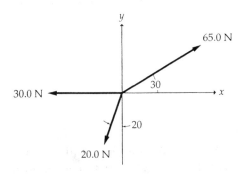

a. 35°
b. 45°
c. 65°
d. 55°
e. 85°

20. If vector **C** is added to vector **D**, the result is a third vector that is perpendicular to **D** and has a magnitude equal to 3D. What is the ratio of the magnitude of **C** to that of **D**?

a. 1.8
b. 2.2
c. 3.2
d. 1.3
e. 1.6

21. A child starts at one corner of a cubical jungle gym in a playground and climbs up to the diagonally opposite corner. The original corner is the coordinate origin, and the x-, y- and z-axes are oriented along the jungle gym edges. The length of each side is 2m. The child's displacement is:

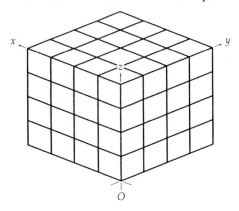

a. 2i + 2j + 2k.
b. 2.8i + 2.8j + 2k
c. 2i + 2j + 2.8k
d. 2i + 2j + 3.5k
e. 3.5i + 3.5j + 3.5k

22.   The displacement of the tip of the 10 cm long minute hand of a clock between 12:15 A.M. and 12:45 P.M. is:

    a.   10 cm, 90°
    b.   10 cm, 180°
    c.   10 cm, 4500°
    d.   20 cm, 180°
    e.   20 cm, 540°

23.   A student decides to spend spring break by driving 50 miles due east, then 50 miles 30 degrees south of east, then 50 miles 30 degrees south of that direction, and to continue to drive 50 miles deviating by 30 degrees each time until he returns to his original position. How far will he drive, and how many vectors must he sum to calculate his displacement?

    a.   0, 0
    b.   0, 8
    c.   0, 12
    d.   400 mi, 8
    e.   600 mi, 12

24.   Jane plans to fly from Binghampton, New York, to Springfield, Massachusetts, about 280 km due east of Binghampton. She heads due east at 280 km/h for one hour but finds herself at Keene, which is 294 km from Binghampton in a direction 17.8 degrees north of due east. What was the wind velocity?

    a.   14 km/h, E
    b.   14 km/h, W
    c.   14 km/h, N
    d.   90 km/h, S
    e.   90 km/h, N

25.   Given that $\mathbf{A} + 2\mathbf{B} = x_1\hat{\mathbf{i}} + y_1\hat{\mathbf{j}}$ and $2\mathbf{A} - \mathbf{B} = x_2\hat{\mathbf{i}} + y_2\hat{\mathbf{j}}$, what is $\mathbf{A}$?

    a. $\mathbf{A} = \dfrac{1}{5}(x_1 + 2x_2)\hat{\mathbf{i}} + \dfrac{1}{5}(y_1 + 2y_2)\hat{\mathbf{j}}$.

    b. $\mathbf{A} = \dfrac{1}{5}(x_1 - 2x_2)\hat{\mathbf{i}} + \dfrac{1}{5}(y_1 - 2y_2)\hat{\mathbf{j}}$

    c. $\mathbf{A} = \dfrac{1}{5}(x_1 + 4x_2)\hat{\mathbf{i}} + \dfrac{1}{5}(y_1 + 2y_2)\hat{\mathbf{j}}$

    d. $\mathbf{A} = \dfrac{1}{5}(x_1 + 4x_2)\hat{\mathbf{i}} + \dfrac{1}{5}(y_1 + 4y_2)\hat{\mathbf{j}}$

    e. $\mathbf{A} = \dfrac{1}{5}(x_1 + 4x_2)\hat{\mathbf{i}} + \dfrac{1}{5}(y_1 - 4y_2)\hat{\mathbf{j}}$

26.   Given that $\mathbf{A} + \mathbf{B} = x_1\hat{\mathbf{i}} + y_1\hat{\mathbf{j}}$ and $\mathbf{A} - \mathbf{B} = x_2\hat{\mathbf{i}} + y_2\hat{\mathbf{j}}$, what is $\mathbf{A}$?

    a. $\mathbf{A} = \frac{1}{2}(x_1 - x_2)\hat{\mathbf{i}} + \frac{1}{2}(y_1 - y_2)\hat{\mathbf{j}}$

    b. $\mathbf{A} = \frac{1}{2}(x_1 + x_2)\hat{\mathbf{i}} + \frac{1}{2}(y_1 - y_2)\hat{\mathbf{j}}$

    c. $\mathbf{A} = \frac{1}{2}(x_1 - x_2)\hat{\mathbf{i}} + \frac{1}{2}(y_1 + y_2)\hat{\mathbf{j}}$

    d. $\mathbf{A} = \frac{1}{2}(x_1 + x_2)\hat{\mathbf{i}} + \frac{1}{2}(y_1 + y_2)\hat{\mathbf{j}}$

    e. $\mathbf{A} = \frac{1}{2}(x_1 + x_2)\hat{\mathbf{i}}$

27.   Given that $\mathbf{A} + \mathbf{B} = x_1\hat{\mathbf{i}} + y_1\hat{\mathbf{j}}$ and $\mathbf{A} - \mathbf{B} = x_2\hat{\mathbf{i}} + y_2\hat{\mathbf{j}}$, what is $\mathbf{B}$?

    a. $\mathbf{B} = \frac{1}{2}(x_1 - x_2)\hat{\mathbf{i}} + \frac{1}{2}(y_1 - y_2)\hat{\mathbf{j}}$

    b. $\mathbf{B} = \frac{1}{2}(x_1 + x_2)\hat{\mathbf{i}} + \frac{1}{2}(y_1 - y_2)\hat{\mathbf{j}}$

    c. $\mathbf{B} = \frac{1}{2}(x_1 - x_2)\hat{\mathbf{i}} + \frac{1}{2}(y_1 + y_2)\hat{\mathbf{j}}$

    d. $\mathbf{B} = \frac{1}{2}(x_1 + x_2)\hat{\mathbf{i}} + \frac{1}{2}(y_1 + y_2)\hat{\mathbf{j}}$

    e. $\mathbf{B} = \frac{1}{2}(y_1 - y_2)\hat{\mathbf{j}}$

28.   The diagram below shows 3 vectors which sum to zero, all of equal length. Which statement below is true?

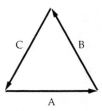

    a.   A + B = A − C
    b.   A + B = B − C
    c.   A − B = 2A − C
    d.   A − B = 2A + C
    e.   2A + 2B = 2C

29.   Which statement is true about the unit vectors **i**, **j** and **k**?

    a.   Their directions are defined by a left-handed coordinate system.
    b.   The angle between any two is 90 degrees.
    c.   Each has a length of 1 m.
    d.   If **i** is directed east and **j** is directed south, **k** points up out of the surface.
    e.   All of the above.

30.   Vectors **A** and **B** have equal magnitudes. Which statement is always true?

    a.   **A** + **B** = 0.
    b.   **A** − **B** = 0.
    c.   **A** − **B** is perpendicular to **A** + **B**.
    d.   **B** − **A** is perpendicular to **A** − **B**.
    e.   The magnitude of **A** − **B** equals the magnitude of **A** + **B**.

31.   When three vectors, **A**, **B**, and **C** are placed head to tail, the vector sum
    A + **B** + **C** = 0. If the vectors all have the same magnitude, the angle between the
    directions of any two adjacent vectors is

    a.   30°
    b.   60°
    c.   90°
    d.   120°
    e.   150°

32.   The vectors **A**, **B**, and **C** are shown below.

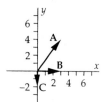

Which diagram below correctly represents **A** + **B** + **C** ?

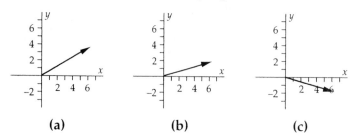

        (a)   (b)   (c)

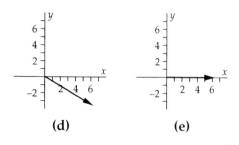

        (d)   (e)

33.   The vectors **A**, **B**, and **C** are shown below.

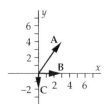

Which diagram below correctly represents **A − B + 2C** ?

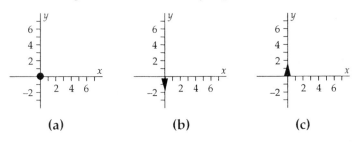

(a)   (b)   (c)

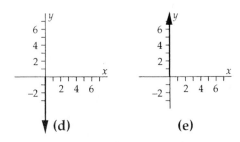

(d)   (e)

34.   The diagram below shows the path taken by a sailboat tacking sideways because it cannot sail directly into the wind.

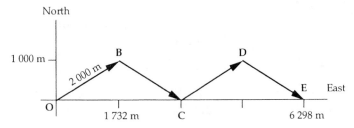

The total distance it travels is

a.   1 000 m.
b.   1 732 m.
c.   2 000 m.
d.   6 298 m.
e.   8 000 m.

35.   The diagram below shows the path taken by a sailboat tacking sideways because it cannot sail directly into the wind.

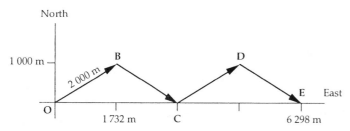

The total displacement of the sailboat, the vector sum of its displacements **OB**, **BC, CD** and **DE**, is

a.   1 732 m, East.
b.   2 000 m, Northeast.
c.   6 298 m, East.
d.   8 000 m, Southeast.
e.   8 000 m, East.

Open-Ended Problems

36.   A hunter wishes to cross a river that is 1.5 km wide and flows with a velocity of 5.0 km/h parallel to its banks. The hunter uses a small powerboat that moves at a maximum speed of 12 km/h with respect to the water. What is the minimum time for crossing?

37.   Raindrops are falling straight downward. When observed from a car traveling at 55 mi/h, the drops streak the side window at an angle of 60° with the vertical. Find the speed with which the drops are falling.

38.   A fast duck is flying $(20\mathbf{i} + 40\mathbf{j})$ mi/h at the same altitude as a slow airplane flying with a velocity of $(-80\mathbf{i} + 40\mathbf{j})$ mi/h. How fast and in what direction is the duck moving relative to the airplane?

39.   Two vectors starting at the same origin have equal and opposite x-components. Is it possible for the two vectors to be perpendicular to each other? Justify your answer.

Chapter 3

Vectors

1.	c		23.	e
2.	a		24.	e
3.	c		25.	a
4.	b		26.	d
5.	d		27.	a
6.	c		28.	d
7.	a		29.	b
8.	b		30.	c
9.	d		31.	d
10.	b		32.	b
11.	d		33.	a
12.	a		34.	e
13.	a		35.	c
14.	e		36.	0.14 h
15	a		37.	31.8 mi/h
16.	c		38.	100 mi/h, along $+i$
17.	d		39.	Yes. If the y-components are of the right magnitudes, the angle can be 90 degrees. (This will occur if $\theta_2 = \theta_1 + \dfrac{\pi}{2}$ and $B = A \tan \theta_1$.)
18.	d			
19.	a			
20.	c			
21.	a			
22.	d			

Chapter 4

Motion in Two Dimensions

Multiple Choice

1. At $t = 0$, a particle leaves the origin with a velocity of 9.0 m/s in the positive y direction and moves in the xy plane with a constant acceleration of $(2.0\mathbf{i} - 4.0\mathbf{j})\,\text{m/s}^2$. At the instant the x coordinate of the particle is 15 m, what is the speed of the particle?

    a. 10 m/s
    b. 16 m/s
    c. 12 m/s
    d. 14 m/s
    e. 26 m/s

2. A particle starts from the origin at $t = 0$ with a velocity of 6.0$\mathbf{i}$ m/s and moves in the xy plane with a constant acceleration of $(-2.0\mathbf{i} + 4.0\mathbf{j})\,\text{m/s}^2$. At the instant the particle achieves its maximum positive x coordinate, how far is it from the origin?

    a. 36 m
    b. 20 m
    c. 45 m
    d. 27 m
    e. 37 m

3. A particle leaves the origin with a velocity of 7.2 m/s in the positive y direction and moves in the xy plane with a constant acceleration of $(3.0\mathbf{i} - 2.0\mathbf{j})\,\text{m/s}^2$. At the instant the particle moves back across the x axis ($y = 0$), what is the value of its x coordinate?

    a. 65 m
    b. 91 m
    c. 54 m
    d. 78 m
    e. 86 m

4.   At $t = 0$, a particle leaves the origin with a velocity of 5.0 m/s in the positive y direction. Its acceleration is given by $\mathbf{a} = (3.0\mathbf{i} - 2.0\mathbf{j})$ m/s^2. At the instant the particle reaches its maximum y coordinate how far is the particle from the origin?

    a.   11 m
    b.   16 m
    c.   22 m
    d.   29 m
    e.   19 m

5.   A particle moves in the xy plane with a constant acceleration given by $\mathbf{a} = -4.0\mathbf{j}$ m/s^2. At $t = 0$, its position and velocity are $10\mathbf{i}$ m and $(-2.0\mathbf{i} + 8.0\mathbf{j})$ m/s, respectively. What is the distance from the origin to the particle at $t = 2.0$ s?

    a.   6.4 m
    b.   10 m
    c.   8.9 m
    d.   2.0 m
    e.   6.2 m

6.   A particle starts from the origin at $t = 0$ with a velocity of $(16\mathbf{i} - 12\mathbf{j})$ m/s and moves in the xy plane with a constant acceleration of $\mathbf{a} = (3.0\mathbf{i} - 6.0\mathbf{j})$ m/s^2. What is the speed of the particle at $t = 2.0$ s?

    a.   52 m/s
    b.   39 m/s
    c.   46 m/s
    d.   33 m/s
    e.   43 m/s

7.   At $t = 0$, a particle leaves the origin with a velocity of 12 m/s in the positive x direction and moves in the xy plane with a constant acceleration of $(-2.0\mathbf{i} + 4.0\mathbf{j})$ m/s^2. At the instant the y coordinate of the particle is 18 m, what is the x coordinate of the particle?

    a.   30 m
    b.   21 m
    c.   27 m
    d.   24 m
    e.   45 m

8.   The initial speed of a cannon ball is 0.20 km/s. If the ball is to strike a target that is at a horizontal distance of 3.0 km from the cannon, what is the minimum time of flight for the ball?

    a.   16 s
    b.   21 s
    c.   24 s
    d.   14 s
    e.   19 s

9.   A ball is thrown horizontally from the top of a building 0.10 km high. The ball strikes the ground at a point 65 m horizontally away from and below the point of release. What is the speed of the ball just before it strikes the ground?

   a.   43 m/s
   b.   47 m/s
   c.   39 m/s
   d.   36 m/s
   e.   14 m/s

10.   A baseball is hit at ground level. The ball is observed to reach its maximum height above ground level 3.0 s after being hit. And 2.5 s after reaching this maximum height, the ball is observed to barely clear a fence that is 97.5 m from where it was hit. How high is the fence?

   a.   8.2 m
   b.   15.8 m
   c.   13.4 m
   d.   11.0 m
   e.   4.9 m

11.   A rock is projected from the edge of the top of a building with an initial velocity of 12.2 m/s at an angle of 53° above the horizontal. The rock strikes the ground a horizontal distance of 25 m from the base of the building. Assume that the ground is level and that the side of the building is vertical. How tall is the building?

   a.   25.3 m
   b.   29.6 m
   c.   27.4 m
   d.   23.6 m
   e.   18.9 m

12.   A projectile is thrown from the top of a building with an initial velocity of 30 m/s in the horizontal direction. If the top of the building is 30 m above the ground, how fast will the projectile be moving just before it strikes the ground?

   a.   35 m/s
   b.   39 m/s
   c.   31 m/s
   d.   43 m/s
   e.   54 m/s

13.   A rifle is aimed horizontally at the center of a large target 60 m away. The initial speed of the bullet is 240 m/s. What is the distance from the center of the target to the point where the bullet strikes the target?

    a.   48 cm
    b.   17 cm
    c.   31 cm
    d.   69 cm
    e.   52 cm

14.   A rock is thrown from the edge of the top of a 100-ft tall building at some unknown angle above the horizontal. The rock strikes the ground a horizontal distance of 160 ft from the base of the building 5.0 s after being thrown. Assume that the ground is level and that the side of the building is vertical. Determine the speed with which the rock was thrown.

    a.   72 ft/s
    b.   77 ft/s
    c.   68 ft/s
    d.   82 ft/s
    e.   87 ft/s

15.   An airplane flies horizontally with a speed of 300 m/s at an altitude of 400 m. Assume that the ground is level. At what horizontal distance from a target must the pilot release a bomb so as to hit the target?

    a.   3.0 km
    b.   2.4 km
    c.   3.3 km
    d.   2.7 km
    e.   1.7 km

16.   An object moving at a constant speed requires 6.0 s to go once around a circle with a diameter of 4.0 m. What is the magnitude of the instantaneous acceleration of the particle during this time?

    a. 2.2 m/s^2
    b. 2.7 m/s^2
    c. 3.3 m/s^2
    d. 3.8 m/s^2
    e. 4.4 m/s^2

17.   A particle moves at a constant speed in a circular path with a radius of 2.06 cm. If
       the particle makes four revolutions each second, what is the magnitude of its
       acceleration?

   a. 20 m/s^2
   b. 18 m/s^2
   c. 13 m/s^2
   d. 15 m/s^2
   e. 24 m/s^2

18.   A race car moving with a constant speed of 60 m/s completes one lap around a
       circular track in 50 s. What is the magnitude of the acceleration of the race car?

   a. 8.8 m/s^2
   b. 7.5 m/s^2
   c. 9.4 m/s^2
   d. 6.3 m/s^2
   e. 5.3 m/s^2

19.   At the lowest point in a vertical dive (radius = 0.58 km), an airplane has a speed
       of 300 km/h which is not changing. Determine the magnitude of the acceleration
       of the pilot at this lowest point.

   a. 26 m/s^2
   b. 21 m/s^2
   c. 16 m/s^2
   d. 12 m/s^2
   e. 8.8 m/s^2

20.   A carnival Ferris wheel has a 15-m radius and completes five turns about its
       horizontal axis every minute. What is the acceleration of a passenger at his
       lowest point during the ride?

   a. 5.7 m/s^2 downward
   b. 4.1 m/s^2 upward
   c. 14 m/s^2 downward
   d. 4.1 m/s^2 downward
   e. 19 m/s^2 downward

21.   A space station of diameter 80 m is turning about its axis at a constant rate. If the
       acceleration of the outer rim of the station is 2.5 m/s², what is the period of
       revolution of the space station?

   a.   22 s
   b.   19 s
   c.   25 s
   d.   28 s
   e.   40 s

22.   A car travels counterclockwise around a flat circle of radius 0.25 km at a constant
       speed of 20 m/s. When the car is at point A as shown in the figure, what is the
       car's acceleration?

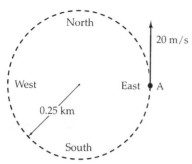

a.   1.6 m/s², east
b.   Zero
c.   1.6 m/s², east
d.   1.6 m/s², north
e.   1.6 m/s², west

23.   A particle moves along a circular path having a radius of 2.0 m. At an instant
       when the speed of the particle is equal to 3.0 m/s and changing at the rate of
       5.0 m/s², what is the magnitude of the total acceleration of the particle?

a.   7.5 m/s²
b.   6.0 m/s²
c.   5.4 m/s²
d.   6.7 m/s²
e.   4.5 m/s²

24.   A car travels in a flat circle of radius R. At a certain instant the velocity of the car
       is 20 m/s north, and the total acceleration of the car is 2.5 m/s² 37° south of west.
       Which of the following is correct?

a.   R = 0.40 km, and the car's speed is decreasing.
b.   R = 0.20 km, and the car's speed is decreasing.
c.   R = 0.20 km, and the car's speed is increasing.
d.   R = 0.16 km, and the car's speed is increasing.
e.   R = 0.16 km, and the car's speed is decreasing.

25.   A car travels in a flat circle of radius R. At a certain instant the velocity of the car
       is 24 m/s west, and the total acceleration of the car is 2.5 m/s² 53° north of west.
       Which of the following is correct?

a.   R = 0.29 km, and the car's speed is increasing.
b.   R = 0.23 km, and the car's speed is decreasing.
c.   R = 0.23 km, and the car's speed is increasing.
d.   R = 0.29 km, and the car's speed is decreasing
e.   R = 0.29 km, and the car's speed is constant.

26.   A stunt pilot performs a circular dive of radius 800 m. At the bottom of the dive (point B in the figure) the pilot has a speed of 200 m/s which at that instant is increasing at a rate of 20 m/s². What acceleration does the pilot have at point B?

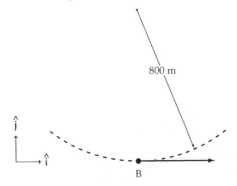

    a. $(50i + 20j)$ m/s²
    b. $(20i - 50j)$ m/s²
    c. $(20i + 50j)$ m/s²
    d. $(-20i + 50j)$ m/s²
    e. $(-50i + 20j)$ m/s²

27.   The speed of a particle moving in a circle 2.0 m in radius increases at the constant rate of 4.4 m/s². At an instant when the magnitude of the total acceleration is 6.0 m/s², what is the speed of the particle?

    a.   3.9 m/s
    b.   2.9 m/s
    c.   3.5 m/s
    d.   3.0 m/s
    e.   1.4 m/s

28.   A car travels in a flat circle of radius R. At a certain instant the velocity of the car is 24 m/s west, and the acceleration of the car has components of 2.4 m/s² east and 1.8 m/s² south. What is the radius of the circle?

    a.   0.24 km
    b.   0.19 km
    c.   0.32 km
    d.   0.14 km
    e.   0.27 km

29.   A particle moves in the xy plane in a circle centered on the origin. At a certain instant the velocity and acceleration of the particle are 6.0**i** m/s and $(3.0\mathbf{i} + 4.0\mathbf{j})$ m/s². What are the x and y coordinates of the particle at this moment?

   a. $x = 0, y = -9.0$ m
   b. $x = 0, y = +7.2$ m
   c. $x = 0, y = +9.0$ m
   d. $x = 0, y = -7.2$ m
   e. $x = 6.0$ m, $y = -9.0$ m

30.   A particle moves in the xy plane in a circle centered on the origin. At a certain instant the velocity and acceleration of the particle are 4.0**j** m/s and $(-3.0\mathbf{i} - 2.0\mathbf{j})$ m/s². What are the x and y coordinates of the particle at this moment?

   a. $x = -4.4$ m, $y = 0$
   b. $x = +5.3$ m, $y = 0$
   c. $x = -5.3$ m, $y = 0$
   d. $x = +4.4$ m, $y = 0$
   e. $x = -1.8$ m, $y = 0$

31.   A 0.14-km wide river flows with a uniform speed of 4.0 m/s toward the east. It takes 20 s for a boat to cross the river to a point directly north of its departure point on the south bank. What is the speed of the boat relative to the water?

   a.   5.7 m/s
   b.   8.5 m/s
   c.   8.1 m/s
   d.   7.0 m/s
   e.   6.4 m/s

32.   A 0.20-km wide river has a uniform flow speed of 4.0 m/s toward the east. It takes 20 s for a boat to cross the river to a point directly north of its departure point on the south bank. In what direction must the boat be pointed in order to accomplish this?

   a.   23° west of north
   b.   20° west of north
   c.   24° west of north
   d.   22° west of north
   e.   17° west of north

33.   A 0.20-km wide river has a uniform flow speed of 3.0 m/s toward the east. A boat with a speed of 8.0 m/s relative to the water leaves the south bank and heads in such a way that it crosses to a point directly north of its departure point. How long does it take the boat to cross the river?

a.   29 s
b.   23 s
c.   25 s
d.   27 s
e.   17 s

34.   A river has a steady speed of 0.30 m/s. A student swims downstream a distance of 1.2 km and returns to the starting point. If the student swims with respect to the water at a constant speed and the downstream portion of the swim requires 20 minutes, how much time is required for the entire swim?

a.   50 minutes
b.   80 minutes
c.   90 minutes
d.   70 minutes
e.   60 minutes

35.   The pilot of an aircraft flies due north relative to the ground in a wind blowing 40 km/h toward the east. If his speed relative to the ground is 80 km/h, what is the speed of his airplane relative to the air?

a.   89 km/h
b.   85 km/h
c.   81 km/h
d.   76 km/h
e.   72 km/h

36.   A car travels in a due northerly direction at a speed of 55 km/h. The traces of rain on the side windows of the car make an angle of 60 degrees with respect to the horizontal. If the rain is falling vertically with respect to the earth, what is the speed of the rain with respect to the earth?

a.   48 km/h
b.   95 km/h
c.   58 km/h
d.   32 km/h
e.   80 km/h

37.   A car travels in an oval path as shown below. $v_A = 25$ m/s, West, and $v_B = 20$ m/s, North. The ratio of the magnitude of the centripetal acceleration at B to that at A, $\dfrac{a_B}{a_A}$ is:

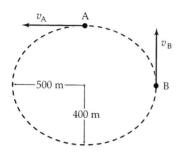

a.   0.512
b.   0.64
c.   0.8
d.   1.25
e.   1.56

38.   Two cooks standing side by side in a restaurant pull their beaters out of the dough at the same instant. A glob of dough flies off each beater. Each glob lands on the top of a tin the same horizontal distance away and at its initial height. However, one lands later than the other. The explanation is that they left the beaters at angles θ_1 and θ_2 such that:

a. $\theta_2 = -\theta_1$.
b. $\theta_1 + \theta_2 = \dfrac{\pi}{4}$.
c. $\theta_1 + \theta_2 = \dfrac{\pi}{2}$.
d. $\theta_1 + \theta_2 = \pi$.
e. $\theta_1 - \theta_2 = \pi$.

39.   The site from which an airplane takes off is the origin. The x-axis points east; the y-axis points straight up. The position and velocity vectors of the plane at a later time are given by

$$\mathbf{r} = (1.61 \times 10^4 \hat{\mathbf{i}} + 9.00 \times 10^3 \hat{\mathbf{j}}) \text{ m and } \mathbf{v} = (150\hat{\mathbf{i}} - 21\hat{\mathbf{j}}) \frac{\text{m}}{\text{s}}.$$

The magnitude, in meters, of the plane's displacement from the origin is

a. 9.14×10^3.
b. 1.61×10^4.
c. 1.84×10^4.
d. $9.14 \times 10^3 t$.
e. $1.61 \times 10^4 t$.

40. A tennis player wants to slam a serve at **O** so that the ball lands just inside the opposite corner of the court. What should the ratio $\dfrac{v_{0y}}{v_{0x}}$ be for the initial velocity $\mathbf{v_0}$? The time $t = 0$ is the time when the ball is hit by the racket.

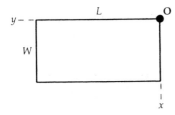

a. W/L

b. L/W

c. $\frac{1}{2}gt^2/L$

d. $\frac{1}{2}gt^2/W$

e. $\frac{1}{2}gt^2/\sqrt{L^2 + W^2}$

41. A tennis player wants to slam a serve at **O** at height h above the court so that the ball lands just inside the opposite corner of the court. The court has length L and width W. What should the ratio $\dfrac{v_{0V}}{v_{0H}}$ be, where v_{0V} is the vertical component and v_{0H} the horizontal component of the initial velocity $\mathbf{v_0}$? The time $t = 0$ is the time when the ball is hit by the racket.

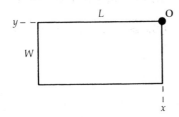

a. $h/\sqrt{L^2 + W^2}$

b. $\left(h - \frac{1}{2}gt^2\right)/\sqrt{L^2 + W^2}$

c. $\left(h + \frac{1}{2}gt^2\right)/\sqrt{L^2 + W^2}$

d. $\sqrt{L^2 + W^2}/\left(h - \frac{1}{2}gt^2\right)$

e. $\sqrt{L^2 + W^2}/\left(h + \frac{1}{2}gt^2\right)$

42.   While her kid brother is on a wooden horse at the edge of a merry-go-round, Sheila rides her bicycle parallel to its edge. The wooden horses have a tangential speed of 6 m/s. Sheila rides at 4 m/s. The radius of the merry-go-round is 8 m. At what time intervals does Sheila encounter her brother, if she rides in the direction of rotation of the merry-go-round?

   a.   5.03 s
   b.   8.37 s
   c.   12.6 s
   d.   25.1 s
   e.   50.2 s

43.   While her kid brother is on a wooden horse at the edge of a merry-go-round, Sheila rides her bicycle parallel to its edge. The wooden horses have a tangential speed of 6 m/s. Sheila rides at 4 m/s. The radius of the merry-go-round is 8 m. At what time intervals does Sheila encounter her brother, if she rides opposite to the direction of rotation of the merry-go-round?

   a.   5.03 s
   b.   8.37 s
   c.   12.6 s
   d.   25.1 s
   e.   50.2 s

44.   Two cars are traveling around identical circular racetracks. Car A travels at a constant speed of 20 m/s. Car B starts at rest and speeds up with constant tangential acceleration until its speed is 40 m/s. When car B has the same (tangential) velocity as car A, it is always true that:

   a.   it is passing car A.
   b.   it has the same linear (tangential) acceleration as car A.
   c.   it has the same centripetal acceleration as car A.
   d.   it has the same total acceleration as car A.
   e.   it has traveled farther than car A since starting.

45.   A student in the front of a school bus tosses a ball to another student in the back of the bus while the bus is moving forward at constant velocity. The *speed* of the ball as seen by a stationary observer in the street:

   a.   is less than that observed inside the bus.
   b.   is the same as that observed inside the bus.
   c.   is greater than that observed inside the bus.
   d.   may be either greater or smaller than that observed inside the bus.
   e.   may be either greater, smaller, or equal to that observed inside the bus.

46.   Two balls, projected at different times so they don't collide, have trajectories A and B, as shown below.

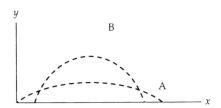

Which statement is correct?

a. v_{0B} must be greater than v_{0A}.
b.   Ball A is in the air for a longer time than ball B.
c.   Ball B is in the air for a longer time than ball A.
d.   Ball B has a greater acceleration than ball A.
e.   Ball A has a greater acceleration than ball B.

47.   The vector **r** indicates the instantaneous displacement of a projectile from the origin. At the instant when the projectile is at **r**, its velocity and acceleration vectors are **v** and **a**. Which statement is correct?

a.   **v** is always perpendicular to **r**.
b.   **a** is always perpendicular to **r**.
c.   **a** is always perpendicular to **v**.
d.   **a** is always perpendicular to $\mathbf{v}_x$.
e.   **a** is always perpendicular to $\mathbf{v}_y$.

48.   A projectile starts at the coordinate origin, where the displacement vector also originates. The initial velocity, $\mathbf{v}_0$, makes an angle θ_0 with the horizontal where $0 < \theta_0 < 90°$. At the instant when the projectile is at the highest point of its trajectory, the displacement, velocity and acceleration vectors are **r**, **v** and **a**. Which statement is true?

a.   **r** is parallel to **v**.
b.   **r** is perpendicular to **v**.
c.   **v** is parallel to **a**.
d.   **v** is perpendicular to **a**.
e.   **r** is perpendicular to **a**.

49.   The site from which an airplane takes off is the origin. The x-axis points east; the y-axis points straight up. The position and vector vectors of the plane at a later time are given by

$$\mathbf{r} = \left(1.61 \times 10^6 \,\hat{\mathbf{i}}\right) \text{m and } \mathbf{v} = +100 \hat{\mathbf{i}} \,\frac{\text{m}}{\text{s}}.$$

The plane is most likely

a.   just touching down.
b.   in level flight in the air.
c.   ascending.
d.   descending.
e.   taking off.

50.   The site from which an airplane takes off is the origin. The x-axis points east; the y-axis points straight up. The position and velocity vectors of the plane at a later time are given by

$$\mathbf{r} = (1.61 \times 10^6 \,\hat{\mathbf{i}} + 9.14 \times 10^3 \,\hat{\mathbf{j}}) \,\text{m and } \mathbf{v} = +224 \hat{\mathbf{i}} \,\frac{\text{m}}{\text{s}}.$$

The plane is most likely

a.   just touching down.
b.   in level flight in the air.
c.   ascending.
d.   descending.
e.   taking off.

51.   The site from which an airplane takes off is the origin. The x-axis points east; the y-axis points straight up. The position and velocity vectors of the plane at a later time are given by

$$\mathbf{r} = (1.61 \times 10^6 \,\hat{\mathbf{i}} + 3.00 \times 10^3 \,\hat{\mathbf{j}}) \,\text{m and } \mathbf{v} = +(150 \hat{\mathbf{i}} - 21 \hat{\mathbf{j}}) \,\frac{\text{m}}{\text{s}}.$$

The plane is most likely

a.   just touching down.
b.   in level flight in the air.
c.   ascending.
d.   descending.
e.   taking off.

52.   The site from which an airplane takes off is the origin. The x-axis points east; the y-axis points straight up. The position and velocity vectors of the plane at a later time are given by

$$\mathbf{r} = (1.61\times10^6\,\hat{\mathbf{i}} + 3.00\times10^3\,\hat{\mathbf{j}})\,\text{m} \text{ and } \mathbf{v} = (150\hat{\mathbf{i}} + 21\hat{\mathbf{j}})\,\frac{\text{m}}{\text{s}}.$$

The plane is most likely

   a.   just touching down.
   b.   in level flight in the air.
   c.   ascending.
   d.   descending.
   e.   taking off.

Open-Ended Problems

53.   Wiley Coyote has missed the elusive roadrunner once again. This time, he leaves the edge of the cliff at 50 m/s horizontal velocity. If the canyon is 100 m deep, how far from the edge of the cliff does the coyote land?

54.   A track star in the broad jump goes into the jump at 12 m/s and launches himself at 20° above the horizontal. How long is he in the air before returning to Earth?

55.   An artillery shell is fired with an initial velocity of 300 m/s at 55° above the horizontal. It explodes on a mountainside 42 s after firing. If x is horizontal and y vertical, find the (x, y) coordinates where the shell explodes.

56.   A football is thrown upward at a 30° angle to the horizontal. To throw a 40.0-m pass, what must be the initial speed of the ball?

57.   A satellite is in a circular orbit 600 km above the Earth's surface. The acceleration of gravity is 8.21 m/s^2 at this altitude. The radius of the Earth is 6400 km. Determine the speed of the satellite, and the time to complete one orbit around the Earth.

58.   A tennis player standing 12.6 m from the net hits the ball at 3.0° above the horizontal. To clear the net, the ball must rise at least 0.33 m. If the ball just clears the net at the apex of its trajectory, how fast was the ball moving when it left the racket?

59.   A rifle is aimed horizontally toward the center of a target 0.10 km away, but the bullet strikes 10 cm below the center. Calculate the velocity of the bullet just as it emerges from the rifle.

Chapter 4

Motion in Two Dimensions

1.	a	29.	a
2.	b	30.	b
3.	d	31.	c
4.	a	32.	d
5.	b	33.	d
6.	d	34.	d
7.	c	35.	a
8.	a	36.	b
9.	b	37.	a
10.	c	38.	c
11.	d	39.	c
12.	b	40.	b
13.	c	41.	b
14.	c	42.	d
15.	d	43.	a
16.	a	44.	c
17.	c	45.	e
18.	b	46.	c
19.	d	47.	d
20.	b	48.	d
21.	c	49.	a
22.	e	50.	b
23.	d	51.	d
24.	b	52.	c
25.	a	53.	226 m
26.	c	54.	0.84 s
27.	b	55.	7.22 km, 1.68 km
28.	c	56.	21.3 m/s

57.   7580 m/s, 5800 s

58.   48.6 m/s

59.   700 m/s

Chapter 5

The Laws of Motion

Multiple Choice

1. In the figure, if the tension in string 1 is 34 N and the tension in string 2 is 24 N, what is the mass of the object shown?

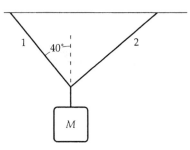

 a. 7.3 kg
 b. 5.5 kg
 c. 1.8 kg
 d. 3.7 kg
 e. 4.5 kg

2. If $M = 2.0$ kg, what is the tension in string 1?

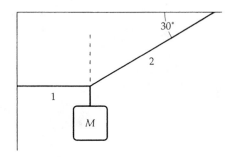

 a. 1.2 N
 b. 11 N
 c. 34 N
 d. 3.5 N
 e. 40 N

3.   If $M = 6.0$ kg, what is the tension in string 1?

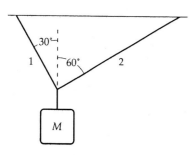

a.   39 N
b.   34 N
c.   29 N
d.   44 N
e.   51 N

4.   If $M = 1.1$ kg, what is the tension in string 1?

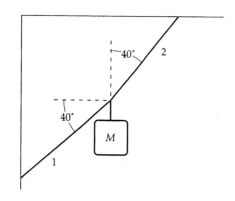

a.   54 N
b.   47 N
c.   40 N
d.   62 N
e.   57 N

5.   An object of unknown weight is suspended as shown. The tension in rope 1 is
      25 lb, and the tension in rope 2 is 31 lb. What is the weight of the suspended
      object?

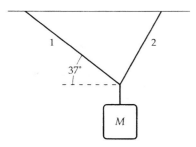

a.   36 lb
b.   33 lb
c.   41 lb
d.   39 lb
e.   56 lb

6.   If $\alpha = 40°$, $\beta = 60°$, and $M = 4.0$ kg, determine the tension in string 1.

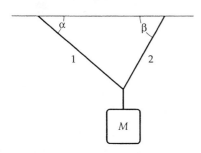

a.   15 N
b.   22 N
c.   17 N
d.   20 N
e.   36 N

7.   If $\alpha = 40°$ and the tension in string 2 is 30 N, determine M.

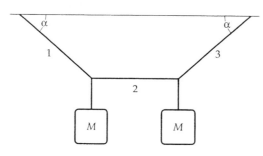

a.   3.4 kg
b.   3.6 kg
c.   2.6 kg
d.   4.9 kg
e.   7.5 kg

8.   Two forces are the only forces acting on a 3.0-kg object which moves with an acceleration of 3.0 m/s² in the positive y direction. If one of the forces acts in the positive x direction and has a magnitude of 8.0 N, what is the magnitude of the other force?

a.   12 N
b.   14 N
c.   16 N
d.   18 N
e.   22 N

9.   The horizontal surface on which the block slides is frictionless. If $F = 20$ N and $M = 5.0$ kg, what is the magnitude of the resulting acceleration of the block?

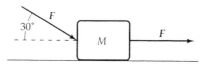

a.   5.3 m/s²
b.   6.2 m/s²
c.   7.5 m/s²
d.   4.7 m/s²
e.   3.2 m/s²

10. The only two forces acting on a body have magnitudes of 20 N and 35 N and directions that differ by 80°. The resulting acceleration has a magnitude of 20 m/s². What is the mass of the body?

    a.   2.4 kg
    b.   2.2 kg
    c.   2.7 kg
    d.   3.1 kg
    e.   1.5 kg

11. If the only forces acting on a 2.0-kg mass are $F_1 = (3i - 8j)$ N and $F_2 = (5i + 3j)$ N, what is the magnitude of the acceleration of the particle?

    a. 1.5 m/s^2
    b. 6.5 m/s^2
    c. 4.7 m/s^2
    d. 9.4 m/s^2
    e. 7.2 m/s^2

12. At an instant when a 4.0-kg object has an acceleration equal to $(5i + 3j)$ m/s², one of the two forces acting on the object is known to be $(12i + 22j)$ N. Determine the magnitude of the other force acting on the object.

    a.   2.0 N
    b.   13 N
    c.   18 N
    d.   1.7 N
    e.   20 N

13. If $F = 4.0$ N and $m = 2.0$ kg, what is the magnitude a of the acceleration for the block shown below? The surface is frictionless.

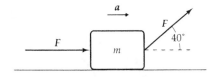

    a. 5.3 m/s^2
    b. 4.4 m/s^2
    c. 3.5 m/s^2
    d. 6.2 m/s^2
    e. 8.4 m/s^2

14.   A block is pushed up a frictionless 30° incline by an applied force as shown. If
       $F = 25$ N and $M = 3.0$ kg, what is the magnitude of the resulting acceleration of
       the block?

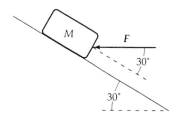

       a.   2.3 m/s^2
       b.   4.6 m/s^2
       c.   3.5 m/s^2
       d.   2.9 m/s^2
       e.   5.1 m/s^2

15.   A 5.0-kg object is suspended by a string from the ceiling of an elevator that is
       accelerating downward at a rate of 2.6 m/s^2. What is the tension in the string?

       a.   49 N
       b.   36 N
       c.   62 N
       d.   13 N
       e.   52 N

16.   The tension in a string from which a 4.0-kg object is suspended in an elevator is
       equal to 44 N. What is the acceleration of the elevator?

       a.   11 m/s^2 upward
       b.   1.2 m/s^2 upward
       c.   1.2 m/s^2 downward
       d.   10 m/s^2 upward
       e.   2.4 m/s^2 downward

17.   A 5.0-kg mass is attached to the ceiling of an elevator by a rope whose mass is
       negligible. What force does the mass exert on the rope when the elevator has an
       acceleration of 4.0 m/s^2 upward?

       a.   69 N downward
       b.   29 N downward
       c.   49 N downward
       d.   20 N downward
       e.   19 N downward

18.   A 5.0-kg mass is suspended by a string from the ceiling of an elevator that is moving upward with a speed which is decreasing at a constant rate of 2.0 m/s in each second. What is the tension in the string supporting the mass?

   a.   49 N
   b.   39 N
   c.   59 N
   d.   10 N
   e.   42 N

19.   A person weighing 0.70 kN rides in an elevator that has an upward acceleration of 1.5 m/s². What is the magnitude of the force of the elevator floor on the person?

   a.   0.11 kN
   b.   0.81 kN
   c.   0.70 kN
   d.   0.59 kN
   e.   0.64 kN

20.   A 3.0-kg block slides on a frictionless 20° inclined plane. A force of 16 N acting parallel to the incline and up the incline is applied to the block. What is the acceleration of the block?

   a.   2.0 m/s² down the incline
   b.   5.3 m/s² up the incline
   c.   2.0 m/s² up the incline
   d.   3.9 m/s² down the incline
   e.   3.9 m/s² up the incline

21.   A 2.0-kg block slides on a frictionless 25° inclined plane. A force of 4.6 N acting parallel to the incline and up the incline is applied to the block. What is the acceleration of the block?

   a.   1.8 m/s² up the incline
   b.   2.3 m/s² up the incline
   c.   6.6 m/s² down the incline
   d.   1.8 m/s² down the incline
   e.   2.3 m/s² down the incline

22.   A 2.0-kg block slides on a frictionless 15° inclined plane. A force acting parallel to the incline is applied to the block. The acceleration of the block is 1.5 m/s² down the incline. What is the applied force?

   a.   8.1 N down the incline
   b.   3.0 N down the incline
   c.   2.1 N up the incline
   d.   3.0 N up the incline
   e.   8.1 N up the incline

23.   A 1.5-kg object has a velocity of 5j m/s at $t = 0$. It is accelerated at a constant rate for five seconds after which it has a velocity of (6i + 12j) m/s. What is the magnitude of the resultant force acting on the object during this time interval?

    a.   3.8 N
    b.   3.2 N
    c.   2.8 N
    d.   4.3 N
    e.   4.6 N

24.   A 1.5-kg object has a velocity of 5j m/s at $t = 0$. It is accelerated at a constant rate for five seconds after which it has a velocity of (6i + 12j) m/s. What is the direction of the resultant force acting on the object during this time interval?

    a.   65°
    b.   56°
    c.   61°
    d.   49°
    e.   27°

25.   A 2.0-kg object has a velocity of 4.0i m/s at $t = 0$. A constant resultant force of (2.0i + 4.0j) N then acts on the object for 3.0 s. What is the magnitude of the object's velocity at the end of the 3.0-s interval?

    a.   9.2 m/s
    b.   6.3 m/s
    c.   8.2 m/s
    d.   7.2 m/s
    e.   7.7 m/s

26.   A 1.5-kg mass has an acceleration of (4.0i − 3.0j) m/s². Only two forces act on the mass. If one of the forces is (2.0i − 1.4j) N, what is the magnitude of the other force?

    a.   4.1 N
    b.   6.1 N
    c.   5.1 N
    d.   7.1 N
    e.   2.4 N

27.   Only two forces act on a 3.0-kg mass. One of the forces is 9.0 N east, and the other is 8.0 N in the direction of 62° north of west. What is the magnitude of the acceleration of the mass?

    a.   2.0 m/s²
    b.   2.4 m/s²
    c.   3.3 m/s²
    d.   2.9 m/s²
    e.   5.7 m/s²

28.   A book is placed on a chair. Then a videocassette is placed on the book. The floor
        exerts a normal force

        a.   on all three.
        b.   only on the book.
        c.   only on the chair.
        d.   upwards on the chair and downwards on the book.
        e.   only on the objects that you have defined to be part of the system.

29.   The apparent weight of a fish in an elevator is greatest when the elevator

        a.   moves downward at constant velocity.
        b.   moves upward at constant velocity.
        c.   accelerates downward.
        d.   accelerates upward.
        e.   is not moving.

30.   The vector sum of three co-planar forces

        a.   must be zero.
        b.   must be perpendicular to one of the three.
        c.   must be parallel to one of the three.
        d.   must be perpendicular to the plane.
        e.   may have any direction in the plane.

31.   When the vector sum of three co-planar forces, **A**, **B** and **C**, is parallel to **A**, we
        can conclude that **B** and **C**

        a.   must sum to zero.
        b.   must be equal and opposite.
        c.   must have equal and opposite components perpendicular to **A**.
        d.   must have equal and opposite components parallel to **A**.
        e.   must have equal and opposite components parallel and perpendicular to **A**.

32.   A constant force is applied to a body that is already moving. The force is directed
        at an angle of 60 degrees to the direction of the body's velocity. What is most
        likely to happen is that

        a.   the body will stop moving.
        b.   the body will move in the direction of the force.
        c.   the body's velocity will increase in magnitude but not change direction.
        d.   the body will gradually change direction more and more toward that of the
               force while speeding up.
        e.   the body will first stop moving and then move in the direction of the force.

33.   A juggler throws two balls up to the same height so that they pass each other halfway up when A is rising and B is descending. Ignore air resistance and buoyant forces. Which statement is true of the two balls at that point?

   a.   There is an residual upward force from the hand on each ball.
   b.   There is a greater residual force from the hand on A than there is on B.
   c.   Only gravity acts on B but there is an additional residual force from the hand on A.
   d.   There is an additional downwards force besides gravity on each ball.
   e.   The only force acting on each ball is the gravitational force.

34.   A bumper car is moving at constant velocity when another bumper car starts to push on it with a constant force at an angle of 60 degrees with respect to the first car's initial velocity. The second bumper car continues pushing in exactly that direction for some time. What is most likely to happen is that

   a.   the first car will stop moving.
   b.   the first car will move in the direction of the force.
   c.   the first car's velocity will increase in magnitude but not change direction.
   d.   the first car's velocity will gradually change direction more and more toward that of the force while increasing in magnitude.
   e.   the first car's velocity will gradually change direction more and more toward that of the force while decreasing in magnitude.

35.   You have a machine which can accelerate pucks on frictionless ice. Starting from rest, the puck travels a distance x in time t when force F is applied. If force $3F$ is applied, the distance the puck travels in time t is

   a. x.
   b. $(3/2)x$.
   c. $3x$.
   d. $(9/2)x$.
   e. $9x$.

36.   A constant force F is applied to a body of mass m that initially is headed east at velocity v_0 until its velocity becomes $-v_0$. The total time of travel is $2t$. The total distance the body travels in that time is

   a. $\dfrac{1}{2}\dfrac{F}{m}t^2$.

   b. $\dfrac{F}{m}t^2$.

   c. $v_0 t - \dfrac{1}{2}\dfrac{F}{m}t^2$.

   d. $v_0 t + \dfrac{1}{2}\dfrac{F}{m}t^2$.

   e. $2\left(v_0 t + \dfrac{1}{2}\dfrac{F}{m}t^2\right)$.

37. The first of two identical boxes of mass m is sitting on level ground. The second box is sitting on a ramp that makes a 20° angle with the ground. The normal force of the level ground on the first box is $\mathbf{N}_L$; the normal force of the ramp on the second box is $\mathbf{N}_R$. Which statement is correct?

    a. $N_R = N_L = mg$.
    b. $N_L = mg$; $N_R = mg \sin 20°$.
    c. $N_L = mg$; $N_R = mg \cos 20°$.
    d. $N_L = mg$; $N_R = -mg \cos 20°$.
    e. $N_R = -N_L = -mg$.

38. The first of two identical boxes of mass m is sitting on level ground. The second box is sitting on a ramp that makes an angle with the ground. When a force of magnitude F is applied to each box in a direction parallel to the surface it is on, upwards on the box on the ramp, neither box moves. Which statement comparing the friction force on the box on the level, f_L, to the friction force on the box on the ramp, f_R, is correct?

    a. $f_R = f_L$.
    b. $f_R > f_L$.
    c. $f_R < f_L$.
    d.   The coefficient of static friction is needed to determine the correct answer.
    e.   The angle between the ramp and the ground is needed to determine the correct answer.

39. The total force needed to drag a box at constant speed across a surface with coefficient of kinetic friction μ_k is least when the force is applied at an angle θ such that

    a. $\sin \theta = \mu_k$.
    b. $\cos \theta = \mu_k$.
    c. $\tan \theta = \mu_k$.
    d. $\cot \theta = \mu_k$.
    e. $\sec \theta = \mu_k$.

40.   A heavy weight is supported by two cables that exert tensions of magnitude T_1 and T_2. Which statement is correct?

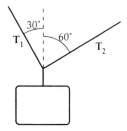

    a. $T_1 = T_2$.
    b. $T_{1y} = T_{2y}$.
    c. $T_1 > T_2$.
    d. $T_1 < T_2$.
    e.   We need the mass of the box in order to determine the correct answer.

41.   Two people, each of 70 kg mass, are riding in an elevator. One is standing on the floor. The other is hanging on a rope suspended from the ceiling. Compare the force $\mathbf{F}_F$ the floor exerts on the first person to the force $\mathbf{F}_R$ the rope exerts on the second person. Which statement is correct?

    a.   They are equal and opposite in direction.
    b.   The are equal and have the same direction.
    c. $\mathbf{F}_R$ is greater than $\mathbf{F}_F$, but they have the same direction.
    d. $\mathbf{F}_R$ is greater than $\mathbf{F}_F$, but they have opposite directions.
    e. $\mathbf{F}_R$ is less than $\mathbf{F}_F$, but they have the same direction.

42.   Two people, each of 70 kg mass, are riding in an elevator. One is standing on the floor. The other is hanging on a rope suspended from the ceiling. Compare the acceleration $\mathbf{a}_F$ of the first person to the acceleration $\mathbf{a}_R$ of the second person. Which statement is correct?

    a.   They are equal and opposite in direction.
    b.   The are equal and have the same direction.
    c.   The acceleration $\mathbf{a}_R$ is greater than $\mathbf{a}_F$, but they have the same direction.
    d.   The acceleration $\mathbf{a}_R$ is greater than $\mathbf{a}_F$, but they have opposite directions.
    e.   The acceleration $\mathbf{a}_R$ is less than $\mathbf{a}_F$, but they have the same direction.

43. The horizontal surface on which the objects slide is frictionless. If $M = 2.0$ kg, the tension in string 1 is 12 N. Determine F.

a.   25 N
b.   20 N
c.   30 N
d.   35 N
e.   40 N

44. The horizontal surface on which the objects slide is frictionless. If $F = 12$ N, what is the tension in string 1?

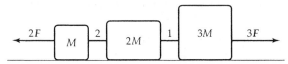

a.   35 N
b.   30 N
c.   40 N
d.   45 N
e.   25 N

45. The surface of the inclined plane shown is frictionless. If $F = 30$ N, what is the magnitude of the force exerted on the 3.0-kg block by the 2.0-kg block?

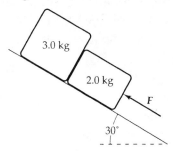

a.   18 N
b.   27 N
c.   24 N
d.   21 N
e.   15 N

46.   If $P = 6.0$ N, what is the magnitude of the force exerted on block 1 by block 2?

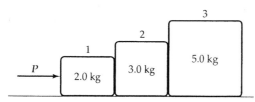

    a.   6.4 N
    b.   5.6 N
    c.   4.8 N
    d.   7.2 N
    e.   8.4 N

47.   If $F = 5.0$ N, what is the magnitude of the force exerted by block 2 on block 1?

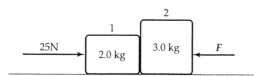

    a.   17 N
    b.   19 N
    c.   21 N
    d.   23 N
    e.   5.0 N

48.   An astronaut who weighs 800 N on the surface of the earth lifts off from planet Zuton in a space ship. The free-fall acceleration on Zuton is 3.0 m/s^2 (down). At the moment of liftoff the acceleration of the space ship is 0.50 m/s^2 (up). What is the magnitude of the force of the space ship on the astronaut?

    a.   41 N
    b.   0.29 kN
    c.   0.24 kN
    d.   0.20 kN
    e.   0.37 kN

49.   The horizontal surface on which the objects slide is frictionless. If $M = 1.0$ kg and the magnitude of the force of the small block on the large block is 5.2 N, determine F.

   a.   6.0 N
   b.   9.0 N
   c.   7.8 N
   d.   4.8 N
   e.   4.1 N

50.   The horizontal surface on which the objects slide is frictionless. If $F = 6.0$ N and $M = 1.0$ kg, what is the magnitude of the force exerted on the large block by the small block?

   a.   7.7 N
   b.   9.8 N
   c.   9.1 N
   d.   8.4 N
   e.   6.5 N

51.   A 6.0-kg object is suspended by a vertical string from the ceiling of an elevator which is accelerating upward at a rate of 1.8 m/s^2. Determine the tension in the string.

   a.   11 N
   b.   70 N
   c.   48 N
   d.   59 N
   e.   62 N

52.   An 8.0-kg object rests on the floor of an elevator which is accelerating downward at a rate of 1.3 m/s^2. What is the magnitude of the force the object exerts on the floor of the elevator?

   a.   59 N
   b.   10 N
   c.   89 N
   d.   68 N
   e.   78 N

53. A 70-kg stunt artist rides in a rocket sled which slides along a flat inclined surface. At an instant when the sled's acceleration has a horizontal component of 6.0 m/s² and a downward component of 2.8m/s², what is the magnitude of the force on the rider by the sled?

   a. 0.83 kN
   b. 0.98 kN
   c. 0.65 kN
   d. 0.68 kN
   e. 0.72 kN

54. If $F = 40$ N and $M = 1.5$ kg, what is the tension in the string connecting M and $2M$? Assume that all surfaces are frictionless.

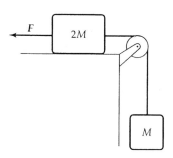

   a. 13 N
   b. 23 N
   c. 36 N
   d. 15 N
   e. 28 N

55. The system shown is released from rest and moves 50 cm in 1.0 s. What is the value of M? All surfaces are frictionless.

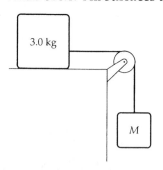

   a. 0.42 kg
   b. 0.34 kg
   c. 0.50 kg
   d. 0.59 kg
   e. 0.68 kg

56.   If $F = 40$ N and $M = 2.0$ kg, what is the magnitude of the acceleration of the suspended object? All surfaces are frictionless.

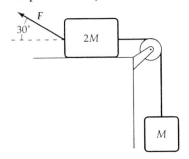

a. 1.2 m/s^2
b. 2.0 m/s^2
c. 1.5 m/s^2
d. 2.5 m/s^2
e. 5.6 m/s^2

57.   If $M = 2.2$ kg, what is the tension in the connecting string? The pulley and all surfaces are frictionless.

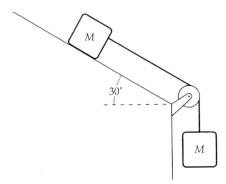

a.   6.4 N
b.   5.9 N
c.   5.4 N
d.   6.9 N
e.   8.3 N

58.   A 5.0-kg mass sits on the floor of an elevator that has a downward acceleration of 1.0 m/s^2. On top of the 5.0-kg mass is an object of unknown mass. The force of the elevator on the 5.0-kg mass is 80 N up. Determine the unknown mass.

a.   3.3 kg
b.   2.4 kg
c.   1.6 kg
d.   4.1 kg
e.   5.0 kg

59.   If the tension, T, is 15 N and the magnitude of the acceleration, a, is 3.0 m/s^2, what is the mass, m, of the suspended object? Assume that all surfaces and the pulley are frictionless?

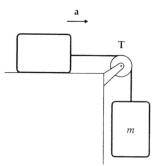

a.   3.1 kg
b.   2.5 kg
c.   2.8 kg
d.   2.2 kg
e.   3.7 kg

60.   If $F = 8.0$ N and $M = 1.0$ kg, what is the tension in the connecting string? The pulley and all surfaces are frictionless.

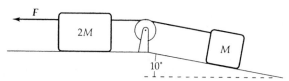

a.   4.1 N
b.   3.5 N
c.   3.8 N
d.   3.1 N
e.   4.8 N

61.   In the figure, if $F = 2.0$ N and $M = 1.0$ kg, what is the tension in the connecting string? The pulley and all surfaces are frictionless.

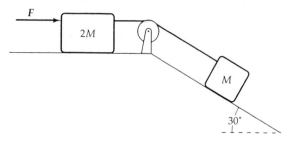

a.   2.6 N
b.   1.1 N
c.   2.1 N
d.   1.6 N
e.   3.7 N

62.   A 4.0-kg block slides down a 35° incline at a constant speed when a 16-N force is
       applied acting up and parallel to the incline. What is the coefficient of kinetic
       friction between the block and the surface of the incline?

       a.   0.20
       b.   0.23
       c.   0.26
       d.   0.33
       e.   0.41

63.   A block is pushed across a horizontal surface by the force shown. If the
       coefficient of kinetic friction between the block and the surface is 0.30, $F = 20$ N,
       $\theta = 30°$, and $M = 3.0$ kg, what is the magnitude of the acceleration of the block?

       a.   2.8 m/s^2
       b.   2.3 m/s^2
       c.   1.8 m/s^2
       d.   3.3 m/s^2
       e.   5.4 m/s^2

64.   A 3.0-kg block moves up a 40° incline with constant speed under the action of a
       26-N force acting up and parallel to the incline. What magnitude force must act
       up and parallel to the incline for the block to move down the incline at constant
       velocity?

       a.   14 N
       b.   12 N
       c.   16 N
       d.   18 N
       e.   25 N

65.   The block shown is pulled across the horizontal surface at a constant speed by the force shown. If M = 5.0 kg, F = 14 N and θ = 35°, what is the coefficient of kinetic friction between the block and the horizontal surface?

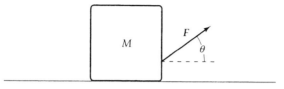

    a.   0.44
    b.   0.33
    c.   0.38
    d.   0.28
    e.   0.17

66.   A box rests on the (horizontal) back of a truck. The coefficient of static friction between the box and the surface on which it rests is 0.24. What maximum distance can the truck travel (starting from rest and moving horizontally with constant acceleration) in 3.0 s without having the box slide?

    a.   14 m
    b.   11 m
    c.   19 m
    d.   24 m
    e.   29 m

67.   In a game of shuffleboard (played on a horizontal surface), a puck is given an initial speed of 6.0 m/s. It slides a distance of 9.0 m before coming to rest. What is the coefficient of kinetic friction between the puck and the surface?

    a.   0.20
    b.   0.18
    c.   0.15
    d.   0.13
    e.   0.27

68.   A 2.0-kg block slides on a rough horizontal surface. A force (magnitude P = 4.0 N) acting parallel to the surface is applied to the block. The magnitude of the block's acceleration is 1.2 m/s². If P is increased to 5.0 N, determine the magnitude of the block's acceleration.

    a.   2.1 m/s²
    b.   2.3 m/s²
    c.   1.9 m/s²
    d.   1.7 m/s²
    e.   3.2 m/a²

69.   A 4.0-kg block is pushed up a 36° incline by a force of magnitude P applied
        parallel to the incline. When P is 31 N, it is observed that the block moves up the
        incline with a constant speed. What value of P would be required to lower the
        block down the incline at a constant speed?

        a.   27 N
        b.   15 N
        c.   13 N
        d.   17 N
        e.   19 N

70.   A 1.8-kg block is released from rest at the top of a rough 30° inclined plane. As
        the block slides down the incline, its acceleration is 3.0 m/s^2 down the incline.
        Determine the magnitude of the force of friction acting on the block.

        a.   4.2 N
        b.   3.0 N
        c.   3.4 N
        d.   3.8 N
        e.   2.3 N

71.   A 1.8-kg block is projected up a rough 10° inclined plane. As the block slides up
        the incline, its acceleration is 3.8 m/s^2 down the incline. What is the magnitude
        of the force of friction acting on the block?

        a.   5.0 N
        b.   3.8 N
        c.   4.2 N
        d.   4.6 N
        e.   6.5 N

72.   A 2.0-kg block slides on a rough horizontal surface. A force ($P = 6.0$ N) is applied
        to the block as shown. The magnitude of the block's acceleration is 1.2 m/s^2.
        What is the magnitude of the force of friction acting on the block?

        a.   2.0 N
        b.   1.4 N
        c.   1.6 N
        d.   2.8 N
        e.   3.4 N

73.   A 3.0-kg block slides on a rough horizontal surface. A force of 8.0 N acting parallel to the surface is applied to the block. The coefficient of kinetic friction between the block and the surface is 0.15. What is the magnitude of the block's acceleration?

   a. 1.9 m/s^2
   b. 1.2 m/s^2
   c. 2.3 m/s^2
   d. 1.5 m/s^2
   e. 2.9 m/s^2

74.   A 1.0-kg block is pushed up a rough 22° inclined plane by a force of 7.0 N acting parallel to the incline. The acceleration of the block is 1.4 m/s^2 up the incline. Determine the magnitude of the force of friction acting on the block.

   a.   1.9 N
   b.   2.2 N
   c.   1.3 N
   d.   1.6 N
   e.   3.3 N

75.   In the figure shown, the coefficient of kinetic friction between the block and the incline is 0.29. What is the magnitude of the acceleration of the suspended block as it falls? Disregard any pulley mass or friction in the pulley.

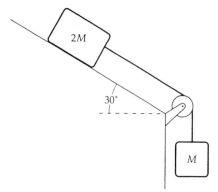

   a. 5.4 m/s^2
   b. 5.2 m/s^2
   c. 4.9 m/s^2
   d. 5.6 m/s^2
   e. 7.9 m/s^2

76. In the figure shown, the coefficient of kinetic friction between the block and the incline is 0.40. What is the magnitude of the acceleration of the suspended block as it falls? Disregard any pulley mass or friction in the pulley.

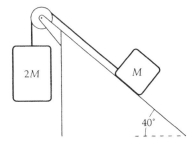

a. 3.4 m/s^2
b. 3.7 m/s^2
c. 4.2 m/s^2
d. 3.9 m/s^2
e. 5.4 m/s^2

77. The three blocks shown are released from rest and are observed to move with accelerations that have a magnitude of 1.5 m/s^2. What is the magnitude of the friction force on the block that slides horizontally? Disregard any pulley mass or friction in the pulley and let M = 2.0 kg.

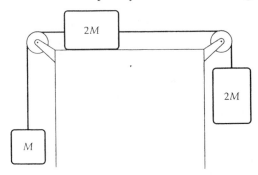

a. 6.0 N
b. 5.1 N
c. 5.5 N
d. 4.6 N
e. 3.7 N

78.   Two blocks in contact with each other are pushed to the right across a rough
horizontal surface by the two forces shown. If the coefficient of kinetic friction
between each of the blocks and the surface is 0.30, determine the magnitude of
the force exerted on the 2.0-kg block by the 3.0-kg block.

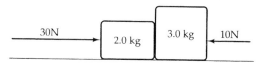

    a.   15 N
    b.   25 N
    c.   11 N
    d.   22 N
    e.   33 N

79.   Two blocks are accelerated across a horizontal frictionless surface as shown.
Frictional forces keep the two blocks from sliding relative to each other, and the
two move with the same acceleration. If $F = 1.2$ N and $M = 1.0$ kg, what is the
horizontal component (frictional force) of the force of the large block on the small
block?

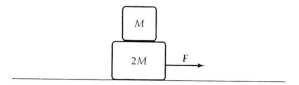

    a.   0.40 N to the left
    b.   0.80 N to the right
    c.   0.40 N to the right
    d.   0.80 N to the left
    e.   1.20 N to the left

80.   The coefficient of kinetic friction between the surface and the larger block is 0.25,
and the coefficient of kinetic friction between the surface and the smaller block is
0.40. If $F = 22$N and $M = 1.0$ kg in the figure, what is the magnitude of the
acceleration of either block?

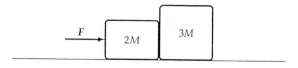

    a. $1.8 \ \text{m/s}^2$
    b. $2.6 \ \text{m/s}^2$
    c. $1.4 \ \text{m/s}^2$
    d. $2.2 \ \text{m/s}^2$
    e. $3.7 \ \text{m/s}^2$

81. In the figure, the coefficient of kinetic friction between the surface and the larger block is 0.20, and the coefficient of kinetic friction between the surface and the smaller block is 0.30. If $F = 14$ N and $M = 1.0$ kg, what is the magnitude of the acceleration of either block?

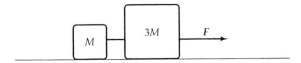

a. 2.0 m/s^2
b. 1.3 m/s^2
c. 1.5 m/s^2
d. 1.8 m/s^2
e. 3.5 m/s^2

82. Two blocks are accelerated across a horizontal frictionless surface as shown. Frictional forces keep the two blocks from sliding relative to each other, and the two move with the same acceleration. If $F = 1.2$ N and $M = 1.0$ kg, what is the horizontal component (frictional force) of the force of the small block on the large block?

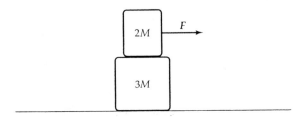

a. 0.48 N to the right
b. 0.72 N to the right
c. 0.72 N to the left
d. 0.48 N to the left
e. 0.65 N to the left

83.   Two blocks connected by a string are pulled across a horizontal surface by a force applied to one of the blocks, as shown. The coefficient of kinetic friction between the blocks and the surface is 0.25. If each block has an acceleration of 2.0 m/s^2 to the right, what is the magnitude F of the applied force?

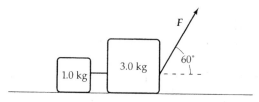

   a.   25 N
   b.   18 N
   c.   11 N
   d.   14 N
   e.   7.0 N

84.   In the figure, the coefficient of kinetic friction between the surface and the larger block is 0.20, and the coefficient of kinetic friction between the surface and the smaller block is 0.30. If $F = 10$ N and $M = 1.0$ kg, what is the tension in the connecting string?

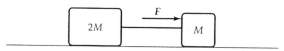

   a.   8.0 N
   b.   6.0 N
   c.   6.7 N
   d.   8.7 N
   e.   3.0 N

85.   The frictional force of the floor on a large suitcase is least when the suitcase is

   a.   pushed by a force parallel to the floor.
   b.   dragged by a force parallel to the floor.
   c.   pulled by a force directed at an angle θ above the floor.
   d.   pushed by a force directed at an angle θ into the floor.
   e.   turned on its side and pushed by a force parallel to the floor.

86.   A 60-kg person rides down an icy hill of 20° slope while standing on a 3.0-kg flat-bottomed bathroom scale. Assume there is no frictional force between the bottom of the scale and the hill. The static friction force the scale exerts on the person is

   a.   0 N.
   b.   201 N.
   c.   211 N.
   d.   553 N.
   e.   580 N.

87.   A chair is placed on a rug. Then a book is placed on the chair. The floor exerts a normal force

    a.   on all three.
    b.   only on the book.
    c.   only on the rug.
    d.   upwards on the rug and downwards on the chair.
    e.   only on the objects you have defined to be part of the system.

88.   Two identical springs with spring constant 50 N/m support a 5.0 N weight as in the picture below. What is the tension in spring A?

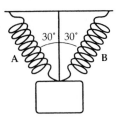

    a.   1.45 N
    b.   2.50 N
    c.   2.89 N
    d.   3.75 N
    e.   5.00 N

89.   Two identical springs with spring constant 50 N/m support a 5.0 N weight as in the picture below. What is the change in length of each spring when the weight is hung on the springs.?

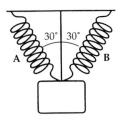

    a.   2.9 cm
    b.   5.0 cm
    c.   5.8 cm
    d.   7.5 cm
    e.   10.0 cm

90.   A book is placed on a chair. Then a videocassette is placed on the book. The floor exerts a normal force

    a.   on all three.
    b.   only on the book.
    c.   only on the chair.
    d.   upwards on the chair and downwards on the book.
    e.   only on the objects that you have defined to be part of the system.

91.   Two bodies, A and B, collide as shown in Figures a and b below.

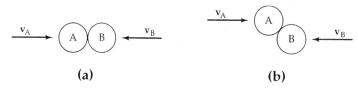

    (a)   **(b)**

Which statement is true?

    a.   They exert equal and opposite forces on each other in (a) but not in (b).
    a.   They exert equal and opposite force on each other in (b) but not in (a).
    c.   They exert equal and opposite force on each other in both (a) and (b).
    d.   The forces are equal and opposite to each other in (a), but only the components of the forces parallel to the velocities are equal in (b).
    e.   The forces are equal and opposite in (a), but only the components of the forces perpendicular to the velocities are equal in (b)

92.   You throw a ball up in the air and hold your hand under it to catch it when it comes down. The reason why the ball stops is because

    a.   your hand is there: your hand exerts no force on the ball.
    b.   your hand exerts a force on the ball perpendicular to its velocity.
    c.   your hand exerts a force on the ball in the direction of its velocity.
    d.   your hand exerts a force on the ball in the direction opposite to its velocity.
    e.   your hand and the ball exert forces in the same direction on each other.

93.   You hold a tennis racket in your hand. On top of the racket you have balanced a ball. Which statement is true?

    a.   The force of your hand on the racket and the force of the ball on the racket are equal and opposite.
    b.   The force of the racket on your hand and the force of the ball on the racket are equal and opposite.
    c.   The force of your hand on the racket and the force of the racket on the ball are equal and opposite.
    d.   The force of the racket on your hand and the force of the racket on the ball are equal and opposite.
    e.   The force of your hand on the racket and the force of the racket on your hand are equal and opposite.

94.   When you drag a toy teddy bear along the floor by a force that is parallel to the floor, the magnitude of the force of friction

    a.   is independent of velocity or acceleration.
    b.   increases when the velocity increases.
    c.   is proportional to the acceleration.
    d.   decreases when the force parallel to the floor increases.
    e.   increases when the force parallel to the floor increases.

95.   In order to jump off the floor, the floor must exert a force on you

    a.   in the direction of and equal to your weight.
    b.   opposite to and equal to your weight.
    c.   in the direction of and less than your weight.
    d.   opposite to and less than your weight.
    e.   opposite to and greater than your weight.

96.   When an acrobat hangs motionless from a pair of rings

    a.   she has no measurable weight.
    b.   her weight depends on the angles the ropes make with the ceiling.
    c.   her weight is reduced by the upward force the rings exert on her.
    d.   her weight is increased by the upward force the rings exert on her.
    e.   she exerts a gravitational force on the Earth that is equal to the sum of the forces the rings exert on her.

97.   Three boxes slide on a frictionless horizontal surface when pulled by a force of magnitude F. When we compare the tensions T_1 and T_2 with the force F, we find that

    a. $T_1 = T_2 = F$.
    b. $T_1 = F > T_2$.
    c. $F > T_1 = T_2$.
    d. $F > T_1 > T_2$.
    e. $F - T_1 < T_1 - T_2$.

98.   Three boxes are pushed across a frictionless horizontal surface as shown. When we compare the normal force $N_{2,5}$ that mass $2m$ exerts on mass $5m$ with the normal force $N_{5,10}$ that mass $5m$ exerts on mass $10m$, we find that

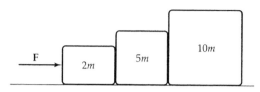

a. $N_{2,5} = N_{5,10} = F$.
b. $N_{2,5} = F > N_{5,10}$.
c. $F > N_{2,5} = N_{5,10}$.
d. $F > N_{2,5} > N_{5,10}$.
e. $F > N_{5,10} > N_{2,5}$.

Open-Ended Problems

99.   A high-diver of mass 70 kg jumps off a board 10 m above the water. If, 2 s after entering the water his downward motion is stopped, what average upward force did the water exert on him?

100.   A 2000-kg sailboat experiences an eastward force of 3000 N by the ocean tide and a wind force against its sails of magnitude 6000 N directed toward the northwest (45° N of W). What is the magnitude and direction of the resultant acceleration?

101.   A box is dropped onto a conveyor belt moving at 2 m/s. If the coefficient of friction between the box and the belt is 0.3, how long before the box moves without slipping?

Chapter 5

The Laws of Motion

1.	d	30.	e
2.	c	31.	c
3.	e	32.	d
4.	c	33.	e
5.	d	34.	d
6.	d	35.	c
7.	c	36.	b
8.	a	37.	c
9.	c	38.	c
10.	b	39.	d
11.	c	40.	c
12.	b	41.	b
13.	c	42.	b
14.	a	43.	b
15.	b	44.	b
16.	b	45.	a
17.	a	46.	c
18.	b	47.	a
19.	b	48.	b
20.	c	49.	c
21.	d	50.	d
22.	c	51.	b
23.	c	52.	d
24.	d	53.	c
25.	a	54.	b
26.	c	55.	b
27.	d	56.	d
28.	c	57.	c
29.	d	58.	d

59.	d		81.	b
60.	c		82.	b
61.	a		83.	a
62.	a		84.	b
63.	c		85.	c
64.	b		86.	a
65.	d		87.	d
66.	b		88.	c
67.	a		89.	c
68.	d		90.	c
69.	b		91.	c
70.	c		92.	d
71.	b		93.	e
72.	d		94.	a
73.	b		95.	e
74.	a		96.	e
75.	c		97.	d
76.	a		98.	d
77.	d		99.	1180 N
78.	d		100.	2.2 m/s^2 at 74° N of W
79.	c		101.	0.7 s
80.	c			

Chapter 6

Circular Motion and Other Applications of Newton's Law

Multiple Choice

1. A race car travels 40 m/s around a banked (45° with the horizontal) circular (radius = 0.20 km) track. What is the magnitude of the resultant force on the 80-kg driver of this car?

    a. 0.68 kN
    b. 0.64 kN
    c. 0.72 kN
    d. 0.76 kN
    e. 0.52 kN

2. An airplane travels 80 m/s as it makes a horizontal circular turn which has a 0.80-km radius. What is the magnitude of the resultant force on the 75-kg pilot of this airplane?

    a. 0.69 kN
    b. 0.63 kN
    c. 0.66 kN
    d. 0.60 kN
    e. 0.57 kN

3. An airplane moves 140 m/s as it travels around a vertical circular loop which has a 1.0-km radius. What is the magnitude of the resultant force on the 70-kg pilot of this plane at the bottom of this loop?

    a. 2.1 kN
    b. 1.4 kN
    c. 0.69 kN
    d. 1.5 kN
    e. 1.3 kN

4. A car travels along the perimeter of a vertical circle (radius = 0.25 km) at a constant speed of 30 m/s. What is the magnitude of the resultant force on the 60-kg driver of the car at the lowest point on this circular path?

    a. 0.37 kN
    b. 0.80 kN
    c. 0.22 kN
    d. 0.59 kN
    e. 0.45 kN

5.   A 30-kg child rides on a circus Ferris wheel that takes her around a vertical
        circular path with a radius of 20 m every 22 s. What is the magnitude of the
        resultant force on the child at the highest point on this trajectory?

        a.   49 N
        b.   0.29 kN
        c.   0.34 kN
        d.   0.25 kN
        e.   0.76 kN

6.   An amusement ride consists of a car moving in a vertical circle on the end of a
        rigid boom. The radius of the circle is 10 m. The combined weight of the car and
        riders is 5.0 kN. At the top of the circle the car has a speed of 5.0 m/s which is
        not changing at that instant. What is the force of the boom on the car at the top of
        the circle?

        a.   3.7 kN (Down)
        b.   1.3 kN (Down)
        c.   6.3 kN (Up)
        d.   3.7 kN (Up)
        e.   5.2 kN (Down)

7.   A highway curve has a radius of 0.14 km and is unbanked. A car weighing 12 kN
        goes around the curve at a speed of 24 m/s without slipping. What is the
        magnitude of the horizontal force of the road on the car?

        a.   12 kN
        b.   17 kN
        c.   13 kN
        d.   5.0 kN
        e.   49 kN

8.   A 4.0-kg mass on the end of a string rotates in a circular motion on a horizontal
        frictionless table. The mass has a constant speed of 2.0 m/s and the radius of the
        circle is 0.80 m. What is the magnitude of the resultant force acting on the mass?

        a.   39 N
        b.   20 N
        c.   44 N
        d.   0 N
        e.   30 N

9.   A stunt pilot weighing 0.70 kN performs a vertical circular dive of radius
        0.80 km. At the bottom of the dive, the pilot has a speed of 0.20 km/s which at
        that instant is not changing. What force does the plane exert on the pilot?

        a.   3.6 kN up
        b.   4.3 kN up
        c.   2.9 kN down
        d.   2.9 kN up
        e.   5.8 kN down

10.   A car travels around an unbanked highway curve (radius 0.15 km) at a constant speed of 25 m/s. What is the magnitude of the resultant force acting on the driver, who weighs 0.80 kN?

    a.   0.87 kN
    b.   0.34 kN
    c.   0.80 kN
    d.   0.00 kN
    e.   0.67 kN

11.   A 0.50-kg mass attached to the end of a string swings in a vertical circle (radius = 2.0 m). When the mass is at the lowest point on the circle, the speed of the mass is 12 m/s. What is the magnitude of the force of the string on the mass at this position?

    a.   31 N
    b.   36 N
    c.   41 N
    d.   46 N
    e.   23 N

12.   A roller-coaster car has a mass of 500 kg when fully loaded with passengers. The car passes over a hill of radius 15 m, as shown. At the top of the hill, the car has a speed of 8.0 m/s. What is the force of the track on the car at the top of the hill?

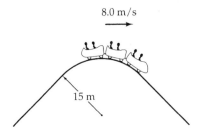

8.0 m/s

15 m

    a.   7.0 kN up
    b.   7.0 kN down
    c.   2.8 kN down
    d.   2.8 kN up
    e.   5.6 kN down

13.   A 0.20-kg object attached to the end of a string swings in a vertical circle (radius = 80 cm). At the top of the circle the speed of the object is 4.5 m/s. What is the magnitude of the tension in the string at this position?

    a.   7.0 N
    b.   2.0 N
    c.   3.1 N
    d.   5.1 N
    e.   6.6 N

14.   A roller-coaster car has a mass of 500 kg when fully loaded with passengers. At the bottom of a circular dip of radius 40 m (as shown in the figure) the car has a speed of 16 m/s. What is the magnitude of the force of the track on the car at the bottom of the dip?

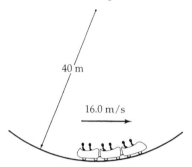

- a.   3.2 kN
- b.   8.1 kN
- c.   4.9 kN
- d.   1.7 kN
- e.   5.3 kN

15.   A 0.50 kg mass attached to the end of a string swings in a vertical circle (radius = 2.0 m). When the mass is at the highest point of the circle the speed of the mass is 8.0 m/s. What is the magnitude of the force of the string on the mass at this position?

- a.   21 N
- b.   11 N
- c.   16 N
- d.   26 N
- e.   36 N

16.   A 50-kg child riding a Ferris wheel (radius = 10 m) travels in a vertical circle. The wheel completes one revolution every 10 s. What is the magnitude of the force on the child by the seat at the highest point on the circular path?

- a.   0.29 kN
- b.   0.49 kN
- c.   0.69 kN
- d.   0.20 kN
- e.   0.40 kN

17.   A 0.30-kg mass attached to the end of a string swings in a vertical circle
       ($R = 1.6$ m), as shown. At an instant when $\theta = 50°$, the tension in the string is
       8.0 N. What is the magnitude of the resultant force on the mass at this instant?

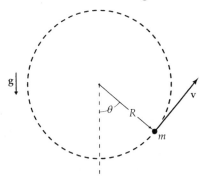

       a.   5.6 N
       b.   6.0 N
       c.   6.5 N
       d.   5.1 N
       e.   2.2 N

18.   An object attached to the end of a string swings in a vertical circle ($R = 1.2$ m), as
       shown. At an instant when $\theta = 30°$, the speed of the object is 5.1 m/s and the
       tension in the string has a magnitude of 20 N. What is the mass of the object?

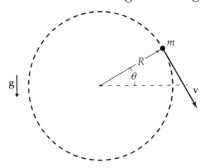

       a.   2.0 kg
       b.   1.5 kg
       c.   1.8 kg
       d.   1.2 kg
       e.   0.80 kg

19.   A 0.40-kg mass attached to the end of a string swings in a vertical circle having a
       radius of 1.8 m. At an instant when the string makes an angle of 40 degrees
       below the horizontal, the speed of the mass is 5.0 m/s. What is the magnitude of
       the tension in the string at this instant?

       a.   9.5 N
       b.   3.0 N
       c.   8.1 N
       d.   5.6 N
       e.   4.7 N

20.   A 0.50-kg mass attached to the end of a string swings in a vertical circle (radius = 2.0 m). When the string is horizontal, the speed of the mass is 8.0 m/s. What is the magnitude of the force of the string on the mass at this position?

    a.   16 N
    b.   17 N
    c.   21 N
    d.   11 N
    e.   25 N

21.   A 4.0-kg mass attached to the end of a string swings in a vertical circle of radius 2.0 m. When the string makes an angle of 35° with the vertical as shown, the speed of the mass is 5.0 m/s. At this instant what is the magnitude of the force the string exerts on the mass?

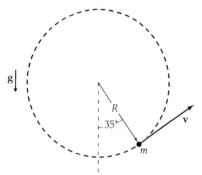

    a.   50 N
    b.   82 N
    c.   89 N
    d.   11 N
    e.   61 N

22.   A split highway has a number of lanes for traffic. For traffic going in one direction, the radius for the inside of the curve is half the radius for the outside. One car, car A, travels on the inside while another car of equal mass, car B, travels at equal speed on the outside of the curve. Which statement about resultant forces on the cars is correct?

    a.   The force on A is half the force on B.
    b.   The force on B is half the force on A.
    c.   The force on A is four times the force on B.
    d.   The force on B is four times the force on A.
    e.   There is no net resultant force on either as long as they stay on the road while turning.

23.   A race car traveling at 100 m/s enters an unbanked turn of 400 m radius. The coefficient of (static) friction between the tires and the track is 1.1. The track has both an inner and an outer wall. Which statement is correct?

a.   The race car will crash into the outer wall.
b.   The race car will crash into the inner wall.
c.   The car will stay in the center of the track.
d.   The car will stay in the center of the track if the driver speeds up.
e.   The car would stay in the center of the track if the radius were reduced to 200 m.

24.   A student is sitting on the right side of a school bus when it makes a right turn. We know that the force of gravity acts downwards and a normal force from the seat acts upwards. If the student stays in place when the bus turns, we also know that there must be

a.   no other force on the student.
b.   a force parallel to the seat directed forward on the student.
c.   a force parallel to the seat directed to the left on the student.
d.   a force parallel to the seat directed to the right on the student.
e.   a force parallel to the seat in a direction between forward and left on the student.

25.   For a plane to be able to fly clockwise in a horizontal circle as seen from above, in addition to exerting a force downwards on the air

a.   it must be increasing its speed.
b.   it must exert a force on the air that is directed to the plane's left side.
c.   it must exert a force on the air that is directed to the plane's right side.
d.   it does not need to exert a force: it must only move the wing flaps out.
e.   it only needs to deflect the air without exerting any additional force on the air.

26.   When a car goes around a circular curve on a level road,

a.   no frictional force is needed because the car simply follows the road.
b.   the frictional force of the road on the car increases when the car's speed decreases.
c.   the frictional force of the road on the car increases when the car's speed increases.
d.   the frictional force of the road on the car increases when the car moves to the outside of the curve.
e.   there is no net frictional force because the road and the car exert equal and opposite forces on each other.

27.   An iceboat is traveling in a circle on the ice. Halfway around the circle the sail and the steering mechanism fall off the boat. Which statement is correct?

   a.   The boat will continue traveling in the circle because there is no friction.
   b.   The boat will continue to travel in the circle because its velocity exerts a force on it.
   c.   The boat will move off on a line tangent to the circle because there is no force on it.
   d.   The boat will move off tangent to the circle because there is a force on it perpendicular to the boat directed to the outside of the circle.
   e.   The boat will move off to the outside perpendicular to the tangent line since a force directed to the outside of the circle always acts on the boat.

28.   A rock attached to a string swings in a vertical circle. Which free body diagram could correctly describe the force(s) on the rock when it is at the highest point?

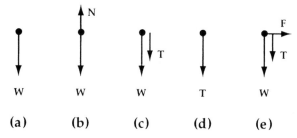

   (a)   (b)   (c)   (d)   (e)

29.   A rock attached to a string swings in a vertical circle. Which free body diagram could correctly describe the force(s) on the rock when the string is in one possible horizontal position?

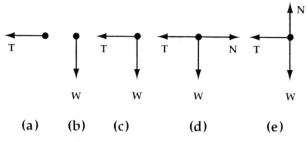

   (a)   (b)   (c)   (d)   (e)

30.   A rock attached to a string swings in a vertical circle. Which free body diagram could correctly describe the force(s) on the rock when it is at the lowest point?

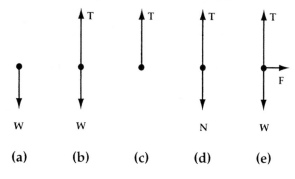

   (a)   (b)   (c)   (d)   (e)

31.   Two small cylindrical plastic containers with flat bottoms are placed on a
       turntable that has a smooth flat surface. Canister A is empty; canister B contains
       lead shot. Each canister is the same distance r from the center. The coefficient of
       static friction between the canisters and the turntable is μ_s. When the speed of
       the turntable is gradually increased,

   a.   only the lighter container slides outward off the turntable; the heavier one
         stays on.
   b.   only the heavier container slides outward off the turntable; the lighter one
         stays on.
   c.   both containers slide off the turntable at the same turntable speed.
   d.   the lighter container slides inward.
   e.   the heavier container slides inward.

32.   A hornet circles around a pop can at constant speed once per second in a path
       with a 12-cm diameter. We can conclude that the hornet's wings must push on
       the air with force components that are

   a.   straight down.
   b.   down and inwards.
   c.   down and outwards.
   d.   down and backwards.
   e.   down, inwards and backwards.

33.   A hornet circles around a pop can at increasing speed while flying in a path with
       a 12-cm diameter. We can conclude that the hornet's wings must push on the air
       with force components that are

   a.   straight down.
   b.   down and inwards.
   c.   down and outwards.
   d.   down and backwards.
   e.   down, backwards and outwards.

Open-Ended Problems

34.   A sample of blood is placed into a centrifuge of radius 15.0 cm. The mass of a red
       corpuscle is 3.0×10^{-16} kg, and the centripetal force required to make it settle out
       of the plasma is 4.0×10^{-11} N. At how many revolutions per second should the
       centrifuge be operated?

35.   A space station in the form of a large wheel, 120 m in diameter, rotates to provide
       an "artificial gravity" of 3.00 m/s^2 for persons located at the outer rim. Find the
       rotational frequency of the wheel (in revolutions per minute) that will produce
       this effect.

36.   An airplane pilot experiences weightlessness as she passes over the top of a loop-
       the-loop maneuver. If her speed is 200 m/s at the time, find the radius of the
       loop.

37.   A race car starts from rest on a circular track of radius 400 m. Its speed increases at the constant rate of 0.500 m/s². At the point where the magnitudes of the radial and tangential accelerations are equal, determine (a) the speed of the race car, and (b) the elapsed time.

Chapter 6

Circular Motion and Other Applications of Newton's Law

1.	b	20.	a	
2.	d	21.	b	
3.	b	22.	b	
4.	c	23.	a	
5.	a	24.	d	
6.	d	25.	b	
7.	d	26.	c	
8.	b	27.	c	
9.	b	28.	c	
10.	b	29.	c	
11.	c	30.	b	
12.	d	31.	c	
13.	c	32.	c	
14.	b	33.	e	
15.	b	34.	150 rev/s (9000 rpm)	
16.	a	35.	2.14 rpm	
17.	c	36.	4080	
18.	d	37.	14.1 m/s, 28.2 s	
19.	c			

Chapter 7

Energy and Energy Transfer

Multiple Choice

1. A constant force of 12 N in the positive x direction acts on a 4.0-kg object as it moves from the origin to the point $(6\mathbf{i} - 8\mathbf{j})$ m. How much work is done by the given force during this displacement?

   a. +60 J
   b. +84 J
   c. +72 J
   d. +48 J
   e. +57 J

2. A 5.0-kg object is pulled along a horizontal surface at a constant speed by a 15-N force acting 20° above the horizontal. How much work is done by this force as the object moves 6.0 m?

   a. 78 J
   b. 82 J
   c. 85 J
   d. 74 J
   e. 43 J

3. A 2.0-kg projectile moves from its initial position to a point that is displaced 20 m horizontally and 15 m above its initial position. How much work is done by the gravitational force on the projectile?

   a. +0.29 kJ
   b. −0.29 kJ
   c. +30 J
   d. −30 J
   e. −50 J

4. How much work is done by a person lifting a 2.0-kg object from the bottom of a well at a constant speed of 2.0 m/s for 5.0 s?

   a. 0.22 kJ
   b. 0.20 kJ
   c. 0.24 kJ
   d. 0.27 kJ
   e. 0.31 kJ

5.   A 2.5-kg object falls vertically downward in a viscous medium at a constant speed of 2.5 m/s. How much work is done by the force the viscous medium exerts on the object as it falls 80 cm?

　　　a.   +2.0 J
　　　b.   +20 J
　　　c.   −2.0 J
　　　d.   −20 J
　　　e.   +40 J

6.   A 2.0-kg particle has an initial velocity of (5i − 4j) m/s. Some time later, its velocity is (7i + 3j) m/s. How much work was done by the resultant force during this time interval, assuming no energy is lost in the process?

　　　a.   17 J
　　　b.   49 J
　　　c.   19 J
　　　d.   53 J
　　　e.   27 J

7.   A block is pushed across a rough horizontal surface from point A to point B by a force (magnitude P = 5.4 N) as shown in the figure. The magnitude of the force of friction acting on the block between A and B is 1.2 N and points A and B are 0.5 m apart. If the kinetic energies of the block at A and B are 4.0 J and 5.6 J, respectively, how much work is done on the block by the force P between A and B?

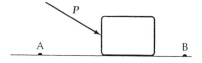

　　　a.   2.7 J
　　　b.   1.0 J
　　　c.   2.2 J
　　　d.   1.6 J
　　　e.   3.2 J

8.   A constant force of 15 N in the negative y direction acts on a particle as it moves from the origin to the point (3i + 3j − 1k) m. How much work is done by the given force during this displacement?

　　　a.   +45 J
　　　b.   −45 J
　　　c.   +30 J
　　　d.   −30 J
　　　e.   +75 J

9.   An object moving along the x axis is acted upon by a force F_x that varies with position as shown. How much work is done by this force as the object moves from $x = 2$ m to $x = 8$ m?

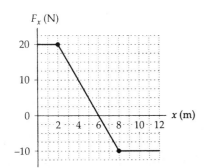

a.   −10 J
b.   +10 J
c.   +30 J
d.   −30 J
e.   +40 J

10.   A body moving along the x axis is acted upon by a force F_x that varies with x as shown. How much work is done by this force as the object moves from $x = 1$ m to $x = 8$ m?

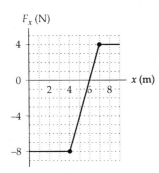

a.   −2 J
b.   −18 J
c.   −10 J
d.   −26 J
e.   +18 J

11.   A force acting on an object moving along the x axis is given by

$$F_x = (14x - 3.0x^2) \text{ N}$$

where x is in m. How much work is done by this force as the object moves from $x = -1$ m to $x = +2$ m?

a.   +12 J
b.   +28 J
c.   +40 J
d.   +42 J
e.   −28 J

12.   The force an ideal spring exerts on an object is given by $F_x = -kx$, where x measures the displacement of the object from its equilibrium ($x = 0$) position. If $k = 60$ N/m, how much work is done by this force as the object moves from $x = -0.20$ m to $x = 0$?

   a.   −1.2 J
   b.   +1.2 J
   c.   +2.4 J
   d.   −2.4 J
   e.   +3.6 J

13.   A 4.0-kg block is lowered down a 37° incline a distance of 5.0 m from point A to point B. A horizontal force ($F = 10$ N) is applied to the block between A and B as shown in the figure. The kinetic energy of the block at A is 10 J and at B it is 20 J. How much work is done on the block by the force of friction between A and B?

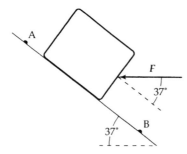

   a.   −58 J
   b.   −53 J
   c.   −68 J
   d.   −63 J
   e.   −47 J

14.   If the resultant force acting on a 2.0-kg object is equal to $(3\mathbf{i} + 4\mathbf{j})$ N, what is the change in kinetic energy as the object moves from $(7\mathbf{i} - 8\mathbf{j})$ m to $(11\mathbf{i} - 5\mathbf{j})$ m?

   a.   +36 J
   b.   +28 J
   c.   +32 J
   d.   +24 J
   e.   +60 J

15.   As a 2.0-kg object moves from $(2\mathbf{i} + 5\mathbf{j})$ m to $(6\mathbf{i} - 2\mathbf{j})$ m, the constant resultant force acting on it is equal to $(4\mathbf{i} - 3\mathbf{j})$ N. If the speed of the object at the initial position is 4.0 m/s, what is its kinetic energy at its final position?

   a.   62 J
   b.   53 J
   c.   73 J
   d.   86 J
   e.   24 J

16.   A block slides on a rough horizontal surface from point A to point B. A force (magnitude $P = 2.0$ N) acts on the block between A and B, as shown. Points A and B are 1.5 m apart. If the kinetic energies of the block at A and B are 5.0 J and 4.0 J, respectively, how much work is done on the block by the force of friction as the block moves from A to B?

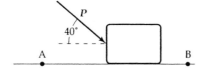

    a.   −3.3 J
    b.   +1.3 J
    c.   +3.3 J
    d.   −1.3 J
    e.   +4.6 J

17.   A 2.0-kg block slides down a frictionless incline from point A to point B. A force (magnitude $P = 3.0$ N) acts on the block between A and B, as shown. Points A and B are 2.0 m apart. If the kinetic energy of the block at A is 10 J, what is the kinetic energy of the block at B?

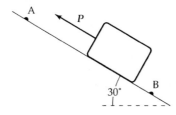

    a.   27 J
    b.   20 J
    c.   24 J
    d.   17 J
    e.   37 J

18.   A 3.0-kg block is dragged over a rough horizontal surface by a constant force of 16 N acting at an angle of 37° above the horizontal as shown. The speed of the block increases from 4.0 m/s to 6.0 m/s in a displacement of 5.0 m. What work was done by the friction force during this displacement?

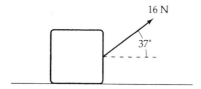

16 N

37°

    a.   −34 J
    b.   −64 J
    c.   −30 J
    d.   −94 J
    e.   +64 J

19.   A 6.0-kg block slides along a horizontal surface. If μ_k = 0.20 for the block and surface, at what rate is the friction force doing work on the block at an instant when its speed is 4.0 m/s?

    a.   −59 W
    b.   −47 W
    c.   −71 W
    d.   −82 W
    e.   +71 W

20.   At what rate is the gravitational force on a 2.0-kg projectile doing work at an instant when the velocity of the projectile is 4.0 m/s directed 30° above the horizontal?

    a.   +39 W
    b.   −78 W
    c.   −39 W
    d.   +78 W
    e.   +25 W

21.   A 2.0-kg block slides down a plane (inclined at 40° with the horizontal) at a constant speed of 5.0 m/s. At what rate is the gravitational force on the block doing work?

    a.   +98 W
    b.   +63 W
    c.   zero
    d.   +75 W
    e.   −75 W

22. The speed of a 4.0-kg object is given by $v = (2t)$ m/s, where t is in s. At what rate is the resultant force on this object doing work at $t = 1$ s?

   a. 48 W
   b. 40 W
   c. 32 W
   d. 56 W
   e. 16 W

23. A 3.0-kg block is on a frictionless horizontal surface. The block is at rest when, at $t = 0$, a force (magnitude $P = 2.0$ N) acting at an angle of 22° above the horizontal is applied to the block. At what rate is the force P doing work at $t = 2.0$ s?

   a. 2.3 W
   b. 2.0 W
   c. 1.4 W
   d. 1.7 W
   e. 1.2 W

24. A 1.6-kg block slides down a plane (inclined at 25° with the horizontal) at a constant speed of 2.0 m/s. At what rate is the frictional force doing work on the block?

   a. +28 W
   b. +13 W
   c. −13 W
   d. −28 W
   e. +6.5 W

25. A 3.0-kg block is on a horizontal surface. The block is at rest when, at $t = 0$, a force (magnitude $P = 12$ N) acting parallel to the surface is applied to the block causing it to accelerate. The coefficient of kinetic friction between the block and the surface is 0.20. At what rate is the force P doing work on the block at $t = 2.0$ s?

   a. 54 W
   b. 49 W
   c. 44 W
   d. 59 W
   e. 24 W

26. Starting from rest at $t = 0$, a 5.0-kg block is pulled across a horizontal surface by a constant horizontal force having a magnitude of 12 N. If the coefficient of friction between the block and the surface is 0.20, at what rate is the 12-N force doing work at $t = 5.0$ s?

   a. 0.13 kW
   b. 0.14 kW
   c. 0.12 kW
   d. 26 W
   e. 12 W

27.   A 10-kg block on a horizontal frictionless surface is attached to a light spring (force constant = 0.80 kN/m). The block is initially at rest at its equilibrium position when a force (magnitude P = 80 N) acting parallel to the surface is applied to the block, as shown. What is the speed of the block when it is 13 cm from its equilibrium position?

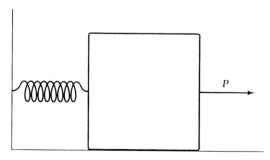

a.   0.85 m/s
b.   0.89 m/s
c.   0.77 m/s
d.   0.64 m/s
e.   0.52 m/s

28.   A 10-kg block on a horizontal frictionless surface is attached to a light spring (force constant = 1.2 kN/m). The block is initially at rest at its equilibrium position when a force (magnitude P) acting parallel to the surface is applied to the block, as shown. When the block is 8.0 cm from the equilibrium position, it has a speed of 0.80 m/s. How much work is done on the block by the force P as the block moves the 8.0 cm?

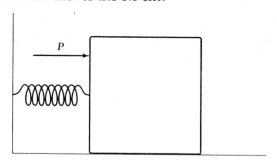

a.   8.3 J
b.   6.4 J
c.   7.0 J
d.   7.7 J
e.   3.9 J

29.   A 20-kg block on a horizontal surface is attached to a light spring
       (force constant = 8.0 kN/m). The block is pulled 10 cm to the right from its
       equilibrium position and released from rest. When the block has moved 2.0 cm
       toward its equilibrium position, its kinetic energy is 13 J. How much work is
       done by the frictional force on the block as it moves the 2.0 cm?

       a.   −2.5 J
       b.   −1.4 J
       c.   −3.0 J
       d.   −1.9 J
       e.   −14 J

30.   The horizontal surface on which the block slides is frictionless. The speed of the
       block before it touches the spring is 6.0 m/s. How fast is the block moving at the
       instant the spring has been compressed 15 cm? k = 2.0 kN/m

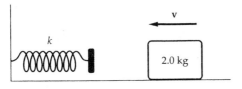

       a.   3.7 m/s
       b.   4.4 m/s
       c.   4.9 m/s
       d.   5.4 m/s
       e.   14 m/s

31.   A 2.0-kg block situated on a frictionless incline is connected to a light spring
       (k = 100 N/m), as shown. The block is released from rest when the spring is
       unstretched. The pulley is frictionless and has negligible mass. What is the speed
       of the block when it has moved 0.20 m down the plane?

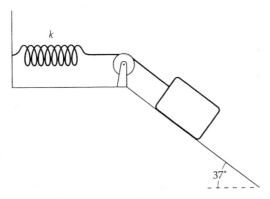

       a.   76 cm/s
       b.   68 cm/s
       c.   60 cm/s
       d.   82 cm/s
       e.   57 cm/s

32.   A 2.0-kg block sliding on a frictionless horizontal surface is attached to one end of a horizontal spring (k = 600 N/m) which has its other end fixed. The speed of the block when the spring is extended 20 cm is equal to 3.0 m/s. What is the maximum speed of this block as it oscillates?

    a.   4.6 m/s
    b.   5.3 m/s
    c.   5.7 m/s
    d.   4.9 m/s
    e.   3.5 m/s

33.   A 10-kg block on a rough horizontal surface is attached to a light spring (force constant = 1.4 kN/m). The block is pulled 8.0 cm to the right from its equilibrium position and released from rest. The frictional force between the block and surface has a magnitude of 30 N. What is the kinetic energy of the block as it passes through its equilibrium position?

    a.   4.5 J
    b.   2.1 J
    c.   6.9 J
    d.   6.6 J
    e.   4.9 J

34.   A 2.0-kg body moving along the x axis has a velocity v_x = 5.0 m/s at x = 0. The only force acting on the object is given by F_x = ($-4.0x$) N, where x is in m. For what value of x will this object first come (momentarily) to rest?

    a.   4.2 m
    b.   3.5 m
    c.   5.3 m
    d.   6.4 m
    e.   5.0 m

35.   A 1.5-kg object moving along the x axis has a velocity of +4.0 m/s at x = 0. If the only force acting on this object is shown in the figure, what is the kinetic energy of the object at x = +3.0 m?

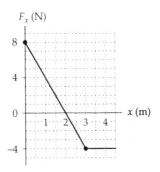

a.   18 J
b.   21 J
c.   23 J
d.   26 J
e.   8 J

36.   The only force acting on a 1.6-kg body as it moves along the x axis is given in the figure. If the velocity of the body at x = 2.0 m is 5.0 m/s, what is its kinetic energy at x = 5.0 m?

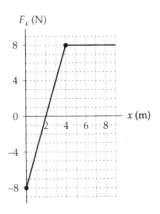

a.   52 J
b.   44 J
c.   36 J
d.   60 J
e.   25 J

37.   The only force acting on a 2.0-kg body moving along the x axis is given by $F_x = (2.0x)$ N, where x is in m. If the velocity of the object at x = 0 is +3.0 m/s, how fast is it moving at x = 2.0 m?

a.   4.2 m/s
b.   3.6 m/s
c.   5.0 m/s
d.   5.8 m/s
e.   2.8 m/s

38.   The only force acting on a 2.0-kg body as it moves along the x axis is given by
$F_x = (12 - 2.0x)$ N, where x is in m. The velocity of the body at $x = 2.0$ m is
$5.5\mathbf{i}$ m/s. What is the maximum kinetic energy attained by the body?

    a.   36 J
    b.   39 J
    c.   43 J
    d.   46 J
    e.   30 J

39.   The only force acting on a 1.8-kg body as it moves along the x axis is given by
$F_x = -(3.0x)$ N, where x is in m. If the velocity of the body at $x = 0$ is $v_x = +8.0$ m/s,
at what value of x will the body have a velocity of $+4.0$ m/s?

    a.   5.7 m
    b.   5.4 m
    c.   4.8 m
    d.   4.1 m
    e.   6.6 m

40.   Two vectors $\mathbf{A}$ and $\mathbf{B}$ are given by $\mathbf{A} = 5\mathbf{i} + 6\mathbf{j} + 7\mathbf{k}$ and $\mathbf{B} = 3\mathbf{i} - 8\mathbf{j} + 2\mathbf{k}$. If these
two vectors are drawn starting at the same point, what is the angle between
them?

    a.   106°
    b.   102°
    c.   110°
    d.   113°
    e.   97°

41.   If $\mathbf{A} = 7\mathbf{i} - 6\mathbf{j} + 5\mathbf{k}$, $|\mathbf{B}| = 7$, and the angle between $\mathbf{A}$ and $\mathbf{B}$ (when the two are
drawn starting from the same point) is 60°, what is the scalar product of these
two vectors?

    a.   −13
    b.   +13
    c.   +37
    d.   −37
    e.   73

42.   If vectors $\mathbf{A}$ and $\mathbf{B}$ have magnitudes 12 and 15, respectively, and the angle
between the two when they are drawn starting from the same point is 110°, what
is the scalar product of these two vectors?

    a.   −76
    b.   −62
    c.   −90
    d.   −47
    e.   −170

43.   If the vectors **A** and **B** have magnitudes of 10 and 11, respectively, and the scalar product of these two vectors is –100, what is the magnitude of the sum of these two vectors?

   a.   6.6
   b.   4.6
   c.   8.3
   d.   9.8
   e.   7.6

44.   If the scalar product of two vectors, **A** and **C**, is equal to –3.5, if $|A| = 2.0$, and the angle between the two vectors when they are drawn starting from the same point is equal to 130°, what is the magnitude of **C**?

   a.   2.1
   b.   2.5
   c.   2.3
   d.   2.7
   e.   3.1

45.   If $A \cdot C = -7.5$, $A = 3i - 4j$, and $|C| = 6.5$, what is the angle between the two vectors when they are drawn starting from the same point?

   a.   118°
   b.   107°
   c.   112°
   d.   103°
   e.   77°

46.   Two vectors **A** and **B** are given by $A = 4i + 8j$ and $B = 6i - 2j$. The scalar product of **A** and a third vector **C** is –16. The scalar product of **B** and **C** is +18. The z component of **C** is 0. What is the magnitude of **C**?

   a.   7.8
   b.   6.4
   c.   3.6
   d.   5.0
   e.   4.8

47.   If **A** = 10, **B** = 15, and α = 130°, determine the scalar product of the two vectors shown.

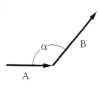

a.   +96
b.   −96
c.   +51
d.   −51
e.   −35

48.   If **A** = 5.0, **B** = 8.0, and α = 30°, determine the scalar product of the two vectors shown.

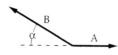

a.   −35
b.   +35
c.   −20
d.   +20
e.   +40

49.   If **A** = 6.0, **B** = 5.0, and α = 40°, determine the scalar product of the two vectors shown.

a.   +19
b.   +23
c.   −19
d.   −23
e.   +30

50.   The same constant force is used to accelerate two carts of the same mass, initially at rest, on horizontal frictionless tracks. The force is applied to cart A for twice as long a time as it is applied to cart B. The work the force does on A is W_A; that on B is W_B. Which statement is correct?

a. $W_A = W_B$.
b. $W_A = \sqrt{2}\, W_B$.
c. $W_A = 2\, W_B$.
d. $W_A = 4\, W_B$.
e. $W_B = 2W_A$.

51.   Carts A and B have equal masses and travel equal distances on straight frictionless tracks while a constant force F is applied to A, and a constant force 2F is applied to B. The relative amounts of work done by the two forces are related by

a. $W_A = 4 W_B$.
b. $W_A = 2 W_B$.
c. $W_A = W_B$.
d. $W_B = 2 W_A$.
e. $W_B = 4 W_A$.

52.   Carts A and B have equal masses and travel equal distances D on side-by-side straight frictionless tracks while a constant force F acts on A and a constant force 2F acts on B. Both carts start from rest. The velocities v_A and v_B of the bodies at the end of distance D are related by

a. $v_B = v_A$.
b. $v_B = \sqrt{2}\, v_A$.
c. $v_B = 2\, v_A$.
d. $v_B = 4\, v_A$.
e. $v_A = 2v_B$.

53.   Two equal masses are raised at constant velocity by ropes that run over pulleys, as shown below. Mass B is raised twice as fast as mass A. The magnitudes of the forces are F_A and F_B, while the power supplied is respectively P_A and P_B. Which statement is correct ?

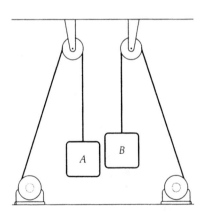

a. $F_B = F_A$; $P_B = P_A$.
b. $F_B = F_A$; $P_B = 2 P_A$.
c. $F_B = 2 F_A$; $P_B = P_A$.
d. $F_B = 2 F_A$; $P_B = 2 P_A$.
e. $P_A = F_A$; $P_B = F_B$.

54.   When a ball rises vertically to a height h and returns to its original point of projection, the work done by the gravitational force is

    a.   0.
    b. $-mgh$.
    c. $+mgh$.
    d. $-2mgh$.
    e. $+2mgh$.

55.   When a crate of mass m is dragged a distance d along a surface with coefficient of kinetic friction μ_k, then dragged back along the same path to its original position, the work done by friction is

    a.   0.
    b. $-\mu_k mgd$.
    c. $+\mu_k mgd$.
    d. $-2\mu_k mgd$.
    e. $+2\mu_k mgd$.

56.   Two balls, A and B, of mass m and 2m respectively, are carried to height h at constant velocity, but B rises twice as fast as A. The work the gravitational force does on B is

    a.   one quarter the work done on A.
    b.   one half the work done on A.
    c.   the same as the work done on A.
    d.   twice the work done on A.
    e.   four times the work done on A.

57.   Equal amounts of work are performed on two bodies, A and B, initially at rest, and of masses M and $2M$ respectively. The relation between their speeds immediately after the work has been done on them is

    a. $v_A = \sqrt{2}v_B$.
    b. $v_A = 2v_B$.
    c. $v_A = v_B$.
    d. $v_B = \sqrt{2}v_A$.
    e. $v_B = 2v_A$.

58. Two cannonballs are dropped from a second floor physics lab at height h above the ground. Ball B has four times the mass of ball A. When the balls pass the bottom of a first floor window at height $\dfrac{h}{4}$ above the ground, the relation between their kinetic energies, K_A and K_B is

   a. $K_A = 4K_B$.
   b. $K_A = 2K_B$.
   c. $K_A = K_B$.
   d. $K_B = 2K_A$.
   e. $K_B = 4K_A$.

59. Two clowns are launched from the same spring-loaded circus cannon with the spring compressed the same distance each time. Clown A has a 40-kg mass; clown B a 60-kg mass. The relation between their kinetic energies at the instant of launch is

   a. $K_A = \dfrac{3}{2}K_B$.

   b. $K_A = \sqrt{\dfrac{3}{2}}K_B$.

   c. $K_A = K_B$.

   d. $K_B = \sqrt{\dfrac{3}{2}}K_A$.

   e. $K_B = \dfrac{3}{2}K_A$.

60. Two clowns are launched from the same spring-loaded circus cannon with the spring compressed the same distance each time. Clown A has a 40-kg mass; clown B a 60-kg mass. The relation between their speeds at the instant of launch is

   a. $v_A = \dfrac{3}{2}v_B$.

   b. $v_A = \sqrt{\dfrac{3}{2}}v_B$.

   c. $v_A = v_B$.

   d. $v_B = \sqrt{\dfrac{3}{2}}v_A$.

   e. $v_B = \dfrac{3}{2}v_A$.

61.   In a contest, two tractors pull two identical blocks of stone the same distance over identical surfaces. However, block A is moving twice as fast as block B when it crosses the finish line. Which statement is correct?

    a.   Block A has twice as much kinetic energy as block B.
    b.   Block B has lost twice as much kinetic energy to friction as block A.
    c.   Block B has lost twice as much kinetic energy as block A.
    d.   Both blocks have had equal losses of energy to friction.
    e.   No energy is lost to friction because the ground has no displacement.

62.   If the scalar (dot) product of two vectors is negative, it means that

    a.   there was a calculator error.
    b.   the angle between the vectors is less than 90 degrees.
    c.   the angle between the vectors is 90 degrees.
    d.   the angle between the vectors is greater than 270 degrees.
    e.   the angle between the vectors is between 90 and 180 degrees.

63.   Two eggs of equal mass are thrown at a blanket with equal velocity. Egg B hits the blanket but egg A hits the wall instead. Compare the work done on the eggs in reducing their velocities to zero.

    a.   More work was done on A than on B.
    b.   More work was done on B than on A.
    c.   The amount of work is the same for both.
    d.   It is meaningless to compare the amount of work because the forces were so different.
    e.   Work was done on B, but no work was done on A because the wall did not move.

64.   Planets go around the sun in elliptical orbits. The highly exaggerated diagram below shows a portion of such an orbit and the force on the planet at one position along that orbit. The planet is moving to the right. $F_{||}$ and $F_{\perp}$ are the components of the force parallel (tangential) and perpendicular (normal) to the orbit. The work they do is $W_{||}$ and $W_{\perp}$. At the position shown

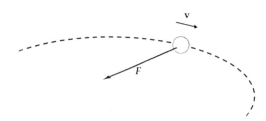

    a. $W_{||}$ slows the planet down; $W_{\perp}$ speeds it up.
    b. $W_{||}$ slows the planet down; $W_{\perp}$ does no work on it.
    c. $W_{||}$ speeds the planet up; $W_{\perp}$ does no work on it.
    d. $W_{||}$ speeds the planet up; $W_{\perp}$ slows it down.
    e. $W_{||}$ does no work on it; $W_{\perp}$ speeds the planet up.

65.   A mass attached to the end of a spring is pulled out and released on a surface
       with friction. The work $\mathbf{F}_{sp} \cdot d\mathbf{x}$ done on the mass by the force exerted by the
       spring

       a.   never has the same sign as the change in energy owing to friction.
       b.   always has the same sign as the change in energy owing to friction.
       c.   has the same sign as the change in energy owing to friction during one half
             of each cycle.
       d.   never has the same sign as the change in energy owing to friction if the force
             of friction is greater than the spring force.
       e.   always has the same sign as the change in energy owing to friction if the
             force of friction is greater than the spring force.

66.   The work $\mathbf{F}_{sp} \cdot d\mathbf{x}$ done by the force exerted by the spring on a mass attached to
       the end of the spring when the mass has displacement $d\mathbf{x}$ is

       a.   always negative.
       b.   always positive.
       c.   negative half the time, positive the other half of the time.
       d.   positive more than it is negative.
       e.   negative more than it is positive.

67.   A 30 kg child sitting 5.0 m from the center of a merry-go-round has a constant
       speed of 5.0 m/s. While she remains seated in the same spot and travels in a
       circle, the work the seat performs on her in one complete rotation is

       a.   0 J.
       b.   150 J.
       c.   1500 J.
       d.   4700 J.
       e.   46,000 J.

Open-Ended Problems

68.   While running, a person dissipates about 0.6 J of mechanical energy per step per
       kilogram of body mass. If a 60-kg person runs with a power of 70 Watts during a
       race, how fast is the person running? Assume a running step is 1.5 m long.

69.   A baseball outfielder throws a baseball of mass 0.15 kg at a speed of 40 m/s and
       initial angle of 30°. What is the kinetic energy of the baseball at the highest point
       of the trajectory?

70.   When an automobile moves with constant velocity the power developed is used
       to overcome the frictional forces exerted by the air and the road. If the power
       developed in an engine is 50.0 hp, what total frictional force acts on the car at
       55 mph (24.6 m/s)? One horsepower equals 746 W.

Chapter 7

Energy and Energy Transfer

1.	c	30.	a
2.	c	31.	c
3.	b	32.	a
4.	b	33.	b
5.	d	34.	b
6.	a	35.	a
7.	c	36.	c
8.	b	37.	b
9.	c	38.	d
10.	d	39.	b
11.	a	40.	b
12.	b	41.	c
13.	c	42.	b
14.	d	43.	b
15.	b	44.	d
16.	a	45.	d
17.	c	46.	c
18.	a	47.	a
19.	b	48.	a
20.	c	49.	d
21.	b	50.	d
22.	e	51.	d
23.	a	52.	b
24.	c	53.	b
25.	b	54.	a
26.	d	55.	d
27.	a	56.	d
28.	c	57.	a
29.	b	58.	e

59.   c

60.   b

61.   d

62.   e

63.   c

64.   b

65.   c

66.   c

67.   a

68.   2.92 m/s

69.   90 J

70.   1520 N

Chapter 8

Potential Energy

Multiple Choice

1. A single conservative force $F_x = (6.0x - 12)$ N (x is in m) acts on a particle moving along the x axis. The potential energy associated with this force is assigned a value of +20 J at $x = 0$. What is the potential energy at $x = 3.0$ m?

    a. +11 J
    b. +29 J
    c. +9.0 J
    d. −9.0 J
    e. +20 J

2. As a particle moves along the x axis it is acted upon by a single conservative force given by $F_x = (20 - 4.0x)$ N where x is in m. The potential energy associated with this force has the value +30 J at the origin ($x = 0$). What is the value of the potential energy at $x = 4.0$ m?

    a. −48 J
    b. +78 J
    c. −18 J
    d. +48 J
    e. +80 J

3. A 0.40-kg particle moves under the influence of a single conservative force. At point A where the particle has a speed of 10 m/s, the potential energy associated with the conservative force is +40 J. As the particle moves from A to B, the force does +25 J of work on the particle. What is the value of the potential energy at point B?

    a. +65 J
    b. +15 J
    c. +35 J
    d. +45 J
    e. −40 J

4. As a 1.0-kg object moves from point A to point B, it is acted upon by a single conservative force which does −40 J of work during this motion. At point A the speed of the particle is 6.0 m/s and the potential energy associated with the force is +50 J. What is the potential energy at point B?

    a. +72 J
    b. +10 J
    c. +90 J
    d. +28 J
    e. +68 J

5.   A 12-kg block on a horizontal frictionless surface is attached to a light spring (force constant = 0.80 kN/m). The block is initially at rest at its equilibrium position when a force (magnitude P = 80 N) acting parallel to the surface is applied to the block, as shown. What is the speed of the block when it is 13 cm from its equilibrium position?

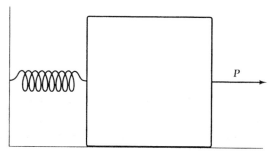

   a.   0.78 m/s
   b.   0.81 m/s
   c.   0.71 m/s
   d.   0.58 m/s
   e.   0.64 m/s

6.   A 7.0-kg block on a horizontal frictionless surface is attached to a light spring (force constant = 1.2 kN/m). The block is initially at rest at its equilibrium position when a force of magnitude P acting parallel to the surface is applied to the block, as shown. When the block is 8.0 cm from the equilibrium position, it has a speed of 0.80 m/s. How much work is done on the block by the force P as the block moves the 8.0 cm?

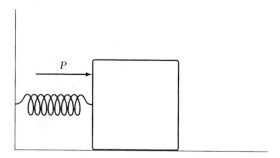

   a.   7.4 J
   b.   5.4 J
   c.   6.1 J
   d.   6.7 J
   e.   4.9 J

7. A 0.60-kg object is suspended from the ceiling at the end of a 2.0-m string. When pulled to the side and released, it has a speed of 4.0 m/s at the lowest point of its path. What maximum angle does the string make with the vertical as the object swings up?

    a.   61°
    b.   54°
    c.   69°
    d.   77°
    e.   47°

8. A pendulum is made by letting a 2.0-kg object swing at the end of a string that has a length of 1.5 m. The maximum angle the string makes with the vertical as the pendulum swings is 30°. What is the speed of the object at the lowest point in its trajectory?

    a.   2.0 m/s
    b.   2.2 m/s
    c.   2.5 m/s
    d.   2.7 m/s
    e.   3.1 m/s

9. A 2.0-kg mass swings at the end of a light string (length = 3.0 m). Its speed at the lowest point on its circular path is 6.0 m/s. What is its kinetic energy at an instant when the string makes an angle of 50° with the vertical?

    a.   21 J
    b.   15 J
    c.   28 J
    d.   36 J
    e.   23 J

10. A 2.5-kg object suspended from the ceiling by a string that has a length of 2.5 m is released from rest with the string 40° below the horizontal position. What is the tension in the string at the instant when the object passes through its lowest position?

    a.   11 N
    b.   25 N
    c.   42 N
    d.   18 N
    e.   32 N

11.   A certain pendulum consists of a 1.5-kg mass swinging at the end of a string
       (length = 2.0 m). At the lowest point in the swing the tension in the string is
       equal to 20 N. To what maximum height above this lowest point will the mass
       rise during its oscillation?

       a.   77 cm
       b.   50 cm
       c.   63 cm
       d.   36 cm
       e.   95 cm

12.   A 0.80-kg object tied to the end of a 2.0-m string swings as a pendulum. At the
       lowest point of its swing, the object has a kinetic energy of 10 J. Determine the
       speed of the object at the instant when the string makes an angle of 50° with the
       vertical.

       a.   5.6 m/s
       b.   4.4 m/s
       c.   3.3 m/s
       d.   5.0 m/s
       e.   6.1 m/s

13.   A 0.04-kg ball is thrown from the top of a 30-m tall building (point A) at an
       unknown angle above the horizontal. As shown in the figure, the ball attains a
       maximum height of 10 m above the top of the building before striking the
       ground at point B. If air resistance is negligible, what is the value of the kinetic
       energy of the ball at B minus the kinetic energy of the ball at A ($K_B - K_A$)?

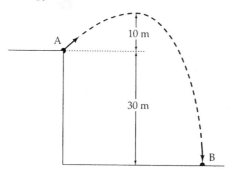

       a.   12 J
       b.   −12 J
       c.   20 J
       d.   −20 J
       e.   32 J

14.   A 1.2-kg mass is projected from ground level with a velocity of 30 m/s at some
       unknown angle above the horizontal. A short time after being projected, the
       mass barely clears a 16-m tall fence. Disregard air resistance and assume the
       ground is level. What is the kinetic energy of the mass as it clears the fence?

    a.   0.35 kJ
    b.   0.73 kJ
    c.   0.40 kJ
    d.   0.68 kJ
    e.   0.19 kJ

15.   A 2.0-kg mass is projected from the edge of the top of a 20-m tall building with a
       velocity of 24 m/s at some unknown angle above the horizontal. Disregard air
       resistance and assume the ground is level. What is the kinetic energy of the mass
       just before it strikes the ground?

    a.   0.18 kJ
    b.   0.97 kJ
    c.   0.89 kJ
    d.   0.26 kJ
    e.   0.40 kJ

16.   A skier weighing 0.70 kN goes over a frictionless circular hill as shown. If the
       skier's speed at point A is 9.2 m/s, what is his speed at the top of the hill (point
       B)?

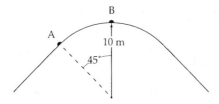

    a.   3.1 m/s
    b.   6.2 m/s
    c.   5.2 m/s
    d.   4.1 m/s
    e.   6.5 m/s

17.   A skier weighing 0.80 kN comes down a frictionless ski run that is circular
       ($R = 30$ m) at the bottom, as shown. If her speed is 12 m/s at point A, what is her
       speed at the bottom of the hill (point B)?

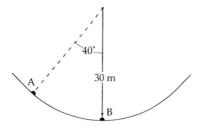

       a.   17 m/s
       b.   19 m/s
       c.   18 m/s
       d.   20 m/s
       e.   12 m/s

18.   A spring ($k = 600$ N/m) is placed in a vertical position with its lower end
       supported by a horizontal surface. The upper end is depressed 20 cm, and a
       4.0-kg block is placed on the depressed spring. The system is then released from
       rest. How far above the point of release will the block rise?

       a.   46 cm
       b.   36 cm
       c.   41 cm
       d.   31 cm
       e.   20 cm

19.   A spring ($k = 200$ N/m) is suspended with its upper end supported from a
       ceiling. With the spring hanging in its equilibrium configuration, an object
       (mass = 2.0 kg) is attached to the lower end and released from rest. What is the
       speed of the object after it has fallen 4.0 cm?

       a.   90 cm/s
       b.   79 cm/s
       c.   96 cm/s
       d.   83 cm/s
       e.   57 cm/s

20.   A 2.0-kg block sliding on a horizontal frictionless surface is attached to one end
       of a horizontal spring ($k = 200$ N/m) which has its other end fixed. If the block
       has a speed of 4.0 m/s as it passes through the equilibrium position, what is its
       speed when it is 20 cm from the equilibrium position?

       a.   2.6 m/s
       b.   3.1 m/s
       c.   3.5 m/s
       d.   1.9 m/s
       e.   2.3 m/s

21. A block (mass = 4.0 kg) sliding on a horizontal frictionless surface is attached to one end of a horizontal spring (k = 100 N/m) which has its other end fixed. If the maximum distance the block slides from the equilibrium position is equal to 20 cm, what is the speed of the block at an instant when it is a distance of 16 cm from the equilibrium position?

   a. 71 cm/s
   b. 60 cm/s
   c. 80 cm/s
   d. 87 cm/s
   e. 57 cm/s

22. A 1.0-kg block is released from rest at the top of a frictionless incline that makes an angle of 37° with the horizontal. An unknown distance down the incline from the point of release, there is a spring with k = 200 N/m. It is observed that the mass is brought momentarily to rest after compressing the spring 0.20 m. How far does the mass slide from the point of release until it is brought momentarily to rest?

   a. 0.98 m
   b. 0.68 m
   c. 0.82 m
   d. 0.55 m
   e. 0.20 m

23. A 20-kg mass is fastened to a light spring (k = 380 N/m) that passes over a pulley as shown. The pulley is frictionless, and the mass is released from rest when the spring is unstretched. After the mass has dropped 0.40 m, what is its speed?

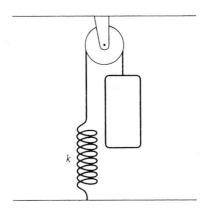

   a. 2.2 m/s
   b. 2.5 m/s
   c. 1.9 m/s
   d. 1.5 m/s
   e. 3.6 m/s

24.   A spring (k = 600 N/m) is at the bottom of a frictionless plane that makes an angle of 30° with the horizontal. The upper end of the spring is depressed 0.10 m, and a 2.0-kg block is placed against the depressed spring. The system is then released from rest. What is the kinetic energy of the block at the instant it has traveled 0.10 m and the spring has returned to its uncompressed length?

    a.   2.0 J
    b.   1.8 J
    c.   2.2 J
    d.   1.6 J
    e.   1.0 J

25.   A spring (k = 600 N/m) is placed in a vertical position with its lower end supported by a horizontal surface. A 2.0-kg block that is initially 0.40 m above the upper end of the spring is dropped from rest onto the spring. What is the kinetic energy of the block at the instant it has fallen 0.50 m (compressing the spring 0.10 m)?

    a.   5.3 J
    b.   6.8 J
    c.   6.3 J
    d.   5.8 J
    e.   6.5 J

26.   A 2.0-kg block slides down a fixed, rough curved track. The block has a speed of 5.0 m/s after its height above a horizontal surface has decreased by 1.8 m. Assume the block starts from rest. How much work is done on the block by the force of friction during this descent?

    a.   −14 J
    b.   −12 J
    c.   −10 J
    d.   −16 J
    e.   −25 J

27.   A 1.5-kg block sliding on a rough horizontal surface is attached to one end of a horizontal spring (k = 200 N/m) which has its other end fixed. If this system is displaced 20 cm horizontally from the equilibrium position and released from rest, the block first reaches the equilibrium position with a speed of 2.0 m/s. What is the coefficient of kinetic friction between the block and the horizontal surface on which it slides?

    a.   0.34
    b.   0.24
    c.   0.13
    d.   0.44
    e.   0.17

28. A 0.75-kg sphere is released from rest and is moving 5.0 m/s after falling 2.0 m in a viscous medium. How much work is done by the force the viscous medium exerts on the sphere during this descent?

    a.   –6.1 J
    b.   –4.6 J
    c.   –5.3 J
    d.   –6.8 J
    e.   –2.7 J

29. A 12-kg projectile is launched with an initial vertical speed of 20 m/s. It rises to a maximum height of 18 m above the launch point. How much work is done by the dissipative (air) resistive force on the projectile during this ascent?

    a.   –0.64 kJ
    b.   –0.40 kJ
    c.   –0.52 kJ
    d.   –0.28 kJ
    e.   –0.76 kJ

30. A 10-kg object is dropped from rest. After falling a distance of 50 m, it has a speed of 26 m/s. How much work is done by the dissipative (air) resistive force on the object during this descent?

    a.   –1.3 kJ
    b.   –1.5 kJ
    c.   –1.8 kJ
    d.   –2.0 kJ
    e.   –2.3 kJ

31. The block shown is released from rest when the spring is stretched a distance d. If $k = 50$ N/m, $m = 0.50$ kg, $d = 10$ cm, and the coefficient of kinetic friction between the block and the horizontal surface is equal to 0.25, determine the speed of the block when it first passes through the position for which the spring is unstretched.

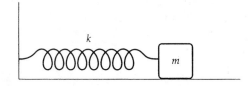

    a.   92 cm/s
    b.   61 cm/s
    c.   71 cm/s
    d.   82 cm/s
    e.   53 cm/s

32.   A 2.0-kg block sliding on a rough horizontal surface is attached to one end of a horizontal spring (k = 250 N/m) which has its other end fixed. The block passes through the equilibrium position with a speed of 2.6 m/s and first comes to rest at a displacement of 0.20 m from equilibrium. What is the coefficient of kinetic friction between the block and the horizontal surface?

        a.   0.32
        b.   0.45
        c.   0.58
        d.   0.19
        e.   0.26

33.   In a given displacement of a particle, its kinetic energy increases by 25 J while its potential energy decreases by 10 J. Determine the work of the nonconservative forces acting on the particle during this displacement.

        a.   −15 J
        b.   +35 J
        c.   +15 J
        d.   −35 J
        e.   +55 J

34.   A particle is acted upon by only two forces, one conservative and one nonconservative, as it moves from point A to point B. The kinetic energies of the particle at points A and B are equal if

        a.   the sum of the works of the two forces is zero.
        b.   the work of the conservative force is equal to the work of the nonconservative force.
        c.   the work of the conservative force is zero.
        d.   the work of the nonconservative force is zero.
        e.   None of the above.

35.   A 1.2-kg mass is projected down a rough circular track (radius = 2.0 m) as shown. The speed of the mass at point A is 3.2 m/s, and at point B, it is 6.0 m/s. How much work is done on the mass between A and B by the force of friction?

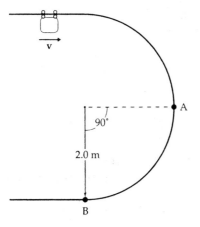

a.   −8.9 J
b.   −7.3 J
c.   −8.1 J
d.   −6.6 J
e.   −24 J

36.   A 1.2-kg mass is projected up a rough circular track (radius = 0.80 m) as shown. The speed of the mass at point A is 8.4 m/s, and at point B, it is 5.6 m/s. How much work is done on the mass between A and B by the force of friction?

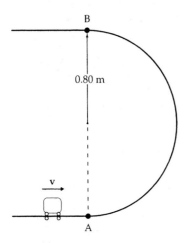

a.   −2.7 J
b.   −8.8 J
c.   −4.7 J
d.   −6.7 J
e.   −19 J

37.   A 3.0-kg mass is dropped from the edge of a 50-m tall building with an initial speed of zero. The mass strikes the ground with a downward velocity of 25 m/s. How much work is done on the mass by air resistance between the point where it is dropped and the point where it strikes the ground?

    a.   −0.46 kJ
    b.   −0.53 kJ
    c.   −0.61 kJ
    d.   −0.38 kJ
    e.   −0.81 kJ

38.   A 2.0-kg mass is projected vertically upward from ground level with an initial speed of 30 m/s. The mass rises to a maximum height of 35 m above ground level. How much work is done on the mass by air resistance between the point of projection and the point of maximum height?

    a.   −0.21 kJ
    b.   −0.47 kJ
    c.   −0.40 kJ
    d.   −0.34 kJ
    e.   −0.69 kJ

39.   A 25-kg block on a horizontal surface is attached to a light spring (force constant = 8.0 kN/m). The block is pulled 10 cm to the right from its equilibrium position and released from rest. When the block has moved 2.0 cm toward its equilibrium position, its kinetic energy is 12 J. How much work is done by the frictional force on the block as it moves the 2.0 cm?

    a.   −4.0 J
    b.   −3.5 J
    c.   −2.4 J
    d.   −2.9 J
    e.   −15 J

40. The two masses in the figure are released from rest. After the 3.0-kg mass has fallen 1.5 m, it is moving with a speed of 3.8 m/s. How much work is done during this time interval by the frictional force on the 2.0 kg mass?

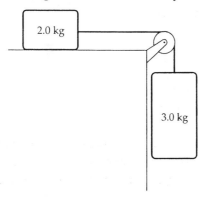

a. −12 J
b. −17 J
c. −20 J
d. −8.0 J
e. −28 J

41. A 2.0-kg block is projected down a plane that makes an angle of 20° with the horizontal with an initial kinetic energy of 2.0 J. If the coefficient of kinetic friction between the block and plane is 0.40, how far will the block slide down the plane before coming to rest?

a. 3.0 m
b. 1.8 m
c. 0.30 m
d. 1.0 m
e. 1.3 m

42. A large spring is used to stop the cars after they come down the last hill of a roller coaster. The cars start at rest at the top of the hill and are caught by a mechanism at the instant their velocities at the bottom are zero. Compare the compression of the spring, x_A, for a fully loaded car with that, x_B, for a lightly loaded car when $m_A = 2m_B$.

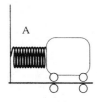 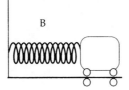

a. $x_A = \dfrac{1}{2} x_B$.
b. $x_A = x_B$.
c. $x_A = \sqrt{2}\, x_B$.
d. $x_A = 2\, x_B$.
e. $x_A = 4\, x_B$.

43.   A small lead sphere of mass m is hung from a spring of spring constant k. The gravitational potential energy of the system equals zero at the equilibrium position of the spring before the weight is attached. The total mechanical energy of the system when the mass is hanging at rest is

   a. $-kx^2$.

   b. $-\dfrac{1}{2}kx^2$.

   c.   0.

   d. $+\dfrac{1}{2}kx^2$.

   e. $+kx^2$.

44.   Cubical blocks of mass m and side ℓ are piled up in a vertical column. The total gravitational potential energy of a column of three blocks is

   a. $\dfrac{5}{2}mg\ell$.

   b. $3mg\ell$.

   c. $\dfrac{9}{2}mg\ell$.

   d. $6mg\ell$.

   e. $9mg\ell$.

45.   An all-terrain vehicle of 2000 kg mass moves up a 15.0° slope at a constant velocity of 6.00 m/s. The rate of change of gravitational potential energy with time is

   a.   5.25 kW.
   b.   24.8 kW.
   c.   30.4 kW.
   d.   118 kW.
   e.   439 kW.

46.   A pendulum bob has potential energy U_0 when held taut in a horizontal position. The bob falls until it is 30° away from the horizontal position, when it has potential energy U_A. It continues to fall until the string is vertical, when it has potential energy U_B. Compare its potential energies at O, A, and B.

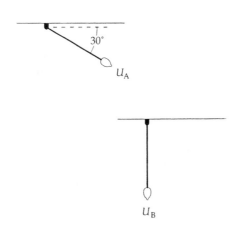

a. $U_0 = U_A = U_B$.
b. $U_A - U_B = 2U_0$.
c. $U_A - U_B = U_0 - U_A$.
d. $U_0 = U_B = 2U_A$.
e. $U_0 - U_A = 2(U_A - U_B)$.

47.   A spring with spring constant $k = 800$ N/m is compressed 12 cm from its equilibrium position. A spring with spring constant $k = 400$ N/m has the same elastic potential energy as the first spring when its extension is

a.   0.060 cm.
b.   0.085 cm.
c.   0.12 cm.
d.   0.17 cm.
e.   0.24 cm.

48.   A spring with spring constant $k = 800$ N/m is extended 12 cm from its equilibrium position. A spring with 6.0 cm extension from equilibrium will have the same potential energy as the first spring if its spring constant is

a.   200 N/m.
b.   400 N/m.
c.   800 N/m.
d.   1600 N/m.
e.   3200 N/m.

49.   A champion athlete can produce one horsepower (746 W) for a short period of time. If a 70-kg athlete were to bicycle to the summit of a 500-m high mountain while expending power at this rate, she would have used at least _____ J of energy.

   a.   746
   b. 3.43×10^5
   c. 3.73×10^5
   d. 7.46×10^5
   e. 2.61×10^7

50.   A champion athlete can produce one horsepower (746 W) for a short period of time. If a 70-kg athlete were to bicycle to the summit of a 500-m high mountain while expending power at this rate, she would reach the summit in _____ seconds.

   a.   1
   b.   460
   c.   500
   d.   1000
   e.   35 000

51.   A champion athlete can produce one horsepower (746 W) for a short period of time. The number of 16 cm high steps a 70 kg athlete could ascend in one minute while expending one horsepower is

   a.   4.
   b.   7.
   c.   65.
   d.   408.
   e.   4567.

52.   Objects A and B, of mass M and $2M$ respectively, are each pushed a distance d straight up an inclined plane by a force F parallel to the plane. The coefficient of kinetic friction between each mass and the plane has the same value μ_k. At the highest point,

   a. $K_A = Fd = K_B$.
   b. $K_A = (F - \mu_k Mg \cos\theta)d$; $K_A = (F - 2\mu_k Mg \cos\theta)d$.
   c. $K_A = (F - Mg \sin\theta)d$; $K_B = (F - 2Mg \sin\theta)d$.
   d. $K_A = (F - Mg \sin\theta - \mu_k Mg \cos\theta)d$; $K_B = (F - Mg \sin\theta - \mu_k Mg \cos\theta)d$.
   e. $K_A = (F - Mg \sin\theta - \mu_k Mg \cos\theta)d$; $K_A = (F - 2Mg \sin\theta - 2\mu_k Mg \cos\theta)d$.

53.   As an object moves from point A to point B only two forces act on it: one force is nonconservative and does −30 J of work, the other force is conservative and does +50 J of work. Between A and B,

    a.   the kinetic energy of object increases, mechanical energy decreases.
    b.   the kinetic energy of object decreases, mechanical energy decreases.
    c.   the kinetic energy of object decreases, mechanical energy increases.
    d.   the kinetic energy of object increases, mechanical energy increases.
    e.   None of the above.

54.   As an object moves from point A to point B only two forces act on it: one force is conservative and does −70 J of work, the other force is nonconservative and does +50 J of work. Between A and B,

    a.   the kinetic energy of object increases, mechanical energy increases.
    b.   the kinetic energy of object decreases, mechanical energy increases.
    c.   the kinetic energy of object decreases, mechanical energy decreases.
    d.   the kinetic energy of object increases, mechanical energy decreases.
    e.   None of the above.

55.   An astronaut tosses a ball out in space where gravitational forces may be neglected. What will happen to the ball?

    a.   It will stop as soon as the force the astronaut gave it is used up.
    b.   It will stop when the energy the astronaut gave it runs out.
    c.   It will stop after a short time because there is no gravity to keep it moving.
    d.   It will move in a circle like a boomerang.
    e.   It will be slowed down very gradually by collisions with molecules in space.

56.   Which of the following is a conservative force? (All refer to a car on a slope.)

    a.   The force you exert on the car pushing it uphill.
    b.   The force exerted by rain drops falling on the car.
    c.   The frictional force of the road on the car.
    d.   The gravitational force acting on the car.
    e.   The force you exert on the car (pushing it uphill) after it starts to slide downhill.

57.   For a force to be a conservative force, when applied to a single test body

    a.   it must have the same value at all points in space.
    b.   it must have the same direction at all points in space.
    c.   it must be parallel to a displacement in any direction.
    d.   equal work must be done in equal displacements.
    e.   no work must be done for motion in closed paths.

58.   The force a spring exerts on a body is a conservative force because

    a.   a spring always exerts a force opposite to the displacement of the body.

    b.   a spring always exerts a force parallel to the displacement of the body.

    c.   the work a spring does on a body is equal for compressions and extensions of equal magnitude.

    d.   the work a spring does on a body is equal and opposite for compressions and extensions of equal magnitude.

    e.   the net work a spring does on a body is zero when the body returns to its initial position.

59.   Identical masses m are attached to identical springs of spring constant k suspended from the ceiling. With both masses hanging in their equilibrium positions, mass A is pulled down 10 cm and released while mass B is pushed up 10 cm and released. Which statement is correct?

    a.   Mass A will travel a smaller distance to its highest point than mass B will travel to its lowest point.

    b.   Mass A will travel a greater distance to its highest point than mass B will travel to its lowest point.

    c.   Masses A and B will travel equal distances between their highest and lowest points.

    d.   More work was done on mass A by the extending force than on mass B by the compressing force.

    e.   The total work done on mass A by the extending force was equal to the total work done on mass B by the compressing force.

60.   Objects A and B, of mass M and $2M$ respectively, are each pushed a distance d straight up an inclined plane by a force F parallel to the plane. The coefficient of kinetic friction between each mass and the plane has the same value μ_k. At the highest point,

    a. $K_A > K_B$.

    b. $K_A = K_B$.

    c. $K_A < K_B$.

    d.   The work done by F on A is greater than the work done by F on B.

    e.   The work done by F on A is less than the work done by F on B.

Open-Ended Problems

61.   A rain cloud contains 2.66×10^7 kg of water vapor. How long would it take for a 2.0 kW pump to lift the same amount of water to an altitude of 2000 m ?

62.   A surprising demonstration involves dropping an egg from a third-floor window to land on a foam-rubber pad 2 in (5 cm) thick without breaking. If a 56-gram egg falls 12 m, and the foam pad stops the egg in 6.25 ms, by how much is the pad compressed?

63.   A 70-kg high jumper leaves the ground with a vertical velocity of 6.0 m/s. How high can he jump?

64.   A simple pendulum, 2.0 m in length, is released from rest when the support string is at an angle of 25° from the vertical. What is the speed of the suspended mass at the bottom of the swing?

Chapter 8

Potential Energy

1.	b	30.	b
2.	c	31.	c
3.	b	32.	b
4.	c	33.	c
5.	a	34.	a
6.	c	35.	c
7.	b	36.	c
8.	a	37.	b
9.	b	38.	a
10.	c	39.	c
11.	d	40.	d
12.	c	41.	a
13.	a	42.	c
14.	a	43.	b
15.	b	44.	c
16.	c	45.	c
17.	a	46.	c
18.	d	47.	d
19.	b	48.	e
20.	c	49.	b
21.	b	50.	b
22.	b	51.	d
23.	a	52.	e
24.	a	53.	a
25.	b	54.	b
26.	c	55.	e
27.	a	56.	d
28.	c	57.	e
29.	d	58.	e

59.   a

60.   a

61.   8.26 years

62.   4.8 cm

63.   1.84 m

64.   1.9 m/s

Chapter 9

Linear Momentum and Collisions

Multiple Choice

1. A 2000-kg truck traveling at a speed of 6.0 m/s makes a 90° turn in a time of 4.0 s and emerges from this turn with a speed of 4.0 m/s. What is the magnitude of the average resultant force on the truck during this turn?

   a. 4.0 kN
   b. 5.0 kN
   c. 3.6 kN
   d. 6.4 kN
   e. 0.67 kN

2. A 1.2-kg object moving with a speed of 8.0 m/s collides perpendicularly with a wall and emerges with a speed of 6.0 m/s in the opposite direction. If the object is in contact with the wall for 2.0 ms, what is the magnitude of the average force on the object by the wall?

   a. 9.8 kN
   b. 8.4 kN
   c. 7.7 kN
   d. 9.1 kN
   e. 1.2 kN

3. A 1.5-kg playground ball is moving with a velocity of 3.0 m/s directed 30° below the horizontal just before it strikes a horizontal surface. The ball leaves this surface 0.50 s later with a velocity of 2.0 m/s directed 60° above the horizontal. What is the magnitude of the average resultant force on the ball?

   a. 14 N
   b. 11 N
   c. 18 N
   d. 22 N
   e. 3.0 N

4.   The only force acting on a 2.0-kg object moving along the x axis is shown. If the velocity v_x is –2.0 m/s at $t = 0$, what is the velocity at $t = 4.0$ s?

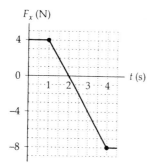

a.   –2.0 m/s
b.   –4.0 m/s
c.   –3.0 m/s
d.   +1.0 m/s
e.   +5.0 m/s

5.   The only force acting on a 2.0-kg object moving along the x axis is shown. If the velocity v_x is +2.0 m/s at $t = 0$, what is the velocity at $t = 4.0$ s?

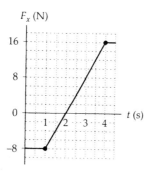

a.   +4.0 m/s
b.   +5.0 m/s
c.   +6.0 m/s
d.   +7.0 m/s
e.   +2.0 m/s

6.   The speed of a 2.0-kg object changes from 30 m/s to 40 m/s during a 5.0-s time interval. During this same time interval, the velocity of the object changes its direction by 90°. What is the magnitude of the average total force acting on the object during this time interval?

a.   30 N
b.   20 N
c.   40 N
d.   50 N
e.   6.0 N

7.   A 3.0-kg ball with an initial velocity of (4i + 3j) m/s collides with a wall and rebounds with a velocity of (−4i + 3j) m/s. What is the impulse exerted on the ball by the wall?

    a.   +24i N s
    b.   −24i N s
    c.   +18j N s
    d.   −18j N s
    e.   +8.0i N s

8.   A 2.4-kg ball falling vertically hits the floor with a speed of 2.5 m/s and rebounds with a speed of 1.5 m/s. What is the magnitude of the impulse exerted on the ball by the floor?

    a.   9.6 N s
    b.   2.4 N s
    c.   6.4 N s
    d.   1.6 N s
    e.   1.0 N s

9.   An 8.0-kg object moving 4.0 m/s in the positive x direction has a one-dimensional collision with a 2.0-kg object moving 3.0 m/s in the opposite direction. The final velocity of the 8.0-kg object is 2.0 m/s in the positive x direction. What is the total kinetic energy of the two-mass system after the collision?

    a.   32 J
    b.   52 J
    c.   41 J
    d.   25 J
    e.   29 J

10.   A 1.6-kg ball is attached to the end of a 0.40-m string to form a pendulum. This pendulum is released from rest with the string horizontal. At the lowest point of its swing, when it is moving horizontally, the ball collides with a 0.80-kg block initially at rest on a horizontal frictionless surface. The speed of the block just after the collision is 3.0 m/s. What is the speed of the ball just after the collision?

    a.   1.7 m/s
    b.   1.1 m/s
    c.   1.5 m/s
    d.   1.3 m/s
    e.   2.1 m/s

11.   A 4.0-kg particle is moving horizontally with a speed of 5.0 m/s when it strikes a vertical wall. The particle rebounds with a speed of 3.0 m/s. What is the magnitude of the impulse delivered to the particle?

   a.   24 N · s
   b.   32 N · s
   c.   40 N · s
   d.   30 N · s
   e.   8.0 N · s

12.   A 2.0-kg object moving with a velocity of 5.0 m/s in the positive x direction strikes and sticks to a 3.0-kg object moving with a speed of 2.0 m/s in the same direction. How much kinetic energy is lost in this collision?

   a.   2.4 J
   b.   9.6 J
   c.   5.4 J
   d.   0.6 J
   e.   6.0 J

13.   A 10-g bullet moving 1000 m/s strikes and passes through a 2.0-kg block initially at rest, as shown. The bullet emerges from the block with a speed of 400 m/s. To what maximum height will the block rise above its initial position?

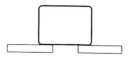

   a.   78 cm
   b.   66 cm
   c.   56 cm
   d.   46 cm
   e.   37 cm

14.   A 12-g bullet moving horizontally strikes and remains in a 3.0-kg block initially at rest on the edge of a table. The block, which is initially 80 cm above the floor, strikes the floor a horizontal distance of 120 cm from its initial position. What was the initial speed of the bullet?

   a.   0.68 km/s
   b.   0.75 km/s
   c.   0.81 km/s
   d.   0.87 km/s
   e.   0.41 km/s

15. A 6.0-kg object moving 5.0 m/s collides with and sticks to a 2.0-kg object. After
     the collision the composite object is moving 2.0 m/s in a direction opposite to the
     initial direction of motion of the 6.0-kg object. Determine the speed of the 2.0-kg
     object before the collision.

     a.   15 m/s
     b.   7.0 m/s
     c.   8.0 m/s
     d.   23 m/s
     e.   11 m/s

16. A 2.0-kg object moving 5.0 m/s collides with and sticks to an 8.0-kg object
     initially at rest. Determine the kinetic energy lost by the system as a result of this
     collision.

     a.   20 J
     b.   15 J
     c.   30 J
     d.   25 J
     e.   5.0 J

17. A 1.6-kg block is attached to the end of a 2.0-m string to form a pendulum. The
     pendulum is released from rest when the string is horizontal. At the lowest point
     of its swing when it is moving horizontally, the block is hit by a 10-g bullet
     moving horizontally in the opposite direction. The bullet remains in the block
     and causes the block to come to rest at the low point of its swing. What was the
     magnitude of the bullet's velocity just before hitting the block?

     a.   1.0 km/s
     b.   1.6 km/s
     c.   1.2 km/s
     d.   1.4 km/s
     e.   1.8 km/s

18. A 3.0-kg mass sliding on a frictionless surface has a velocity of 5.0 m/s east when
     it undergoes a one-dimensional inelastic collision with a 2.0-kg mass that has an
     initial velocity of 2.0 m/s west. After the collision the 3.0-kg mass has a velocity
     of 1.0 m/s east. How much kinetic energy does the two-mass system lose during
     the collision?

     a.   22 J
     b.   24 J
     c.   26 J
     d.   20 J
     e.   28 J

19.   A 3.0-kg mass is released from rest at point A of a circular frictionless track of radius 0.40 m as shown in the figure. The mass slides down the track and collides with a 1.4-kg mass that is initially at rest on a horizontal frictionless surface. If the masses stick together, what is their speed after the collision?

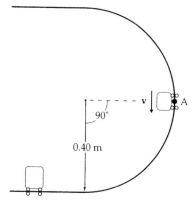

 a. 2.1 m/s
 b. 1.7 m/s
 c. 1.9 m/s
 d. 1.5 m/s
 e. 2.3 m/s

20.   A 3.0-kg mass is sliding on a horizontal frictionless surface with a speed of 3.0 m/s when it collides with a 1.0-kg mass initially at rest as shown in the figure. The masses stick together and slide up a frictionless circular track of radius 0.40 m. To what maximum height, h, above the horizontal surface will the masses slide?

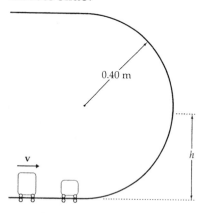

 a. 0.18 m
 b. 0.15 m
 c. 0.21 m
 d. 0.26 m
 e. 0.40 m

21. A 10-g bullet moving horizontally with a speed of 2.0 km/s strikes and passes
     through a 4.0-kg block moving with a speed of 4.2 m/s in the opposite direction
     on a horizontal frictionless surface. If the block is brought to rest by the collision,
     what is the kinetic energy of the bullet as it emerges from the block?

     a.   0.51 kJ
     b.   0.29 kJ
     c.   0.80 kJ
     d.   0.13 kJ
     e.   20 kJ

22. A 10-g bullet moving horizontally with a speed of 1.8 km/s strikes and passes
     through a 5.0-kg block initially at rest on a horizontal frictionless surface. The
     bullet emerges from the block with a speed of 1.0 km/s. What is the kinetic
     energy of the block immediately after the bullet emerges?

     a.   8.0 J
     b.   6.4 J
     c.   5.3 J
     d.   9.4 J
     e.   10 J

23. A pendulum consists of a 2.0-kg block hanging on a 1.5-m length string. A 10-g
     bullet moving with a horizontal velocity of 900 m/s strikes, passes through, and
     emerges from the block (initially at rest) with a horizontal velocity of 300 m/s. To
     what maximum height above its initial position will the block swing?

     a.   32 cm
     b.   38 cm
     c.   46 cm
     d.   27 cm
     e.   9 cm

24. A 1.0-kg ball is attached to the end of a 2.5-m string to form a pendulum. This
     pendulum is released from rest with the string horizontal. At the lowest point in
     its swing when it is moving horizontally, the ball collides elastically with a 2.0-kg
     block initially at rest on a horizontal frictionless surface. What is the speed of the
     block just after the collision?

     a.   2.3 m/s
     b.   4.7 m/s
     c.   3.5 m/s
     d.   3.0 m/s
     e.   7.0 m/s

25.   A 3.0-kg object moving in the positive x direction has a one-dimensional elastic collision with a 5.0-kg object initially at rest. After the collision the 5.0-kg object has a velocity of 6.0 m/s in the positive x direction. What was the initial speed of the 3.0 kg object?

    a.   6.0 m/s
    b.   7.0 m/s
    c.   4.5 m/s
    d.   8.0 m/s
    e.   5.5 m/s

26.   A 3.0-kg object moving 8.0 m/s in the positive x direction has a one-dimensional elastic collision with an object (mass = M) initially at rest. After the collision the object of unknown mass has a velocity of 6.0 m/s in the positive x direction. What is M?

    a.   7.5 kg
    b.   5.0 kg
    c.   6.0 kg
    d.   4.2 kg
    e.   8.0 kg

27.   A 6.0-kg object moving 2.0 m/s in the positive x direction has a one-dimensional elastic collision with a 4.0-kg object moving 3.0 m/s in the opposite direction. What is the total kinetic energy of the two-mass system after the collision?

    a.   30 J
    b.   62 J
    c.   20 J
    d.   44 J
    e.   24 J

28.   Two blocks with masses 2.0 kg and 3.0 kg are placed on a horizontal frictionless surface. A light spring is placed in a horizontal position between the blocks. The blocks are pushed together, compressing the spring, and then released from rest. After contact with the spring ends, the 3.0-kg mass has a speed of 2.0 m/s. How much potential energy was stored in the spring when the blocks were released?

    a.   15 J
    b.   3.0 J
    c.   6.0 J
    d.   12 J
    e.   9.0 J

29. An 80-g particle moving with an initial speed of 50 m/s in the positive x direction strikes and sticks to a 60-g particle moving 50 m/s in the positive y direction. How much kinetic energy is lost in this collision?

    a. 96 J
    b. 89 J
    c. 175 J
    d. 86 J
    e. 110 J

30. A 2.0-kg object moving 3.0 m/s strikes a 1.0-kg object initially at rest. Immediately after the collision, the 2.0-kg object has a velocity of 1.5 m/s directed 30° from its initial direction of motion. What is the x-component of the velocity of the 1.0-kg object just after the collision?

    a. 3.7 m/s
    b. 3.4 m/s
    c. 1.5 m/s
    d. 2.4 m/s
    e. 4.1 m/s

31. A 2.0-kg object moving 3.0 m/s strikes a 1.0-kg object initially at rest. Immediately after the collision, the 2.0-kg object has a velocity of 1.5 m/s directed 30° from its initial direction of motion. What is the y-component of the velocity of the 1.0-kg object just after the collision?

    a. –3.7 m/s
    b. –3.4 m/s
    c. –1.5 m/s
    d. –2.4 m/s
    e. –4.1 m/s

32. A 6.0-kg object, initially at rest in free space, "explodes" into three segments of equal mass. Two of these segments are observed to be moving with equal speeds of 20 m/s with an angle of 60° between their directions of motion. How much kinetic energy is released in this explosion?

    a. 2.4 kJ
    b. 2.9 kJ
    c. 2.0 kJ
    d. 3.4 kJ
    e. 1.2 kJ

33.   A 5.0-g particle moving 60 m/s collides with a 2.0-g particle initially at rest. After
the collision each of the particles has a velocity that is directed 30° from the
original direction of motion of the 5.0-g particle. What is the speed of the 2.0-g
particle after the collision?

   a.   72 m/s
   b.   87 m/s
   c.   79 m/s
   d.   94 m/s
   e.   67 m/s

34.   A 1.0-kg object moving 9.0 m/s collides with a 2.0-kg object moving 6.0 m/s in a
direction that is perpendicular to the initial direction of motion of the 1.0-kg
object. The two masses remain together after the collision, and this composite
object then collides with and sticks to a 3.0-kg object. After these collisions, the
final composite (6.0-kg) object remains at rest. What was the speed of the 3.0-kg
object before the collisions?

   a.   15 m/s
   b.   10 m/s
   c.   5.0 m/s
   d.   20 m/s
   e.   25 m/s

35.   A 3.0-kg mass sliding on a frictionless surface explodes into three 1.0-kg masses.
After the explosion the velocities of the three masses are: (1) 9.0 m/s, north;
(2) 4.0 m/s, 30° south of west; and (3) 4.0 m/s, 30° south of east. What was the
magnitude of the original velocity of the 3.0-kg mass?

   a.   1.7 m/s
   b.   1.0 m/s
   c.   1.3 m/s
   d.   2.0 m/s
   e.   2.8 m/s

36.   A 3.0-kg mass moving in the positive x direction with a speed of 10 m/s collides
with a 6.0-kg mass initially at rest. After the collision, the speed of the 3.0-kg
mass is 8.0 m/s, and its velocity vector makes an angle of 35° with the positive x
axis. What is the magnitude of the velocity of the 6.0-kg mass after the collision?

   a.   2.2 m/s
   b.   2.9 m/s
   c.   4.2 m/s
   d.   3.5 m/s
   e.   4.7 m/s

37.   A 5.0-kg mass with an initial velocity of 4.0 m/s, east collides with a 4.0-kg mass with an initial velocity of 3.0 m/s, west. After the collision the 5.0-kg mass has a velocity of 1.2 m/s, south. What is the magnitude of the velocity of the 4.0-kg mass after the collision?

   a.   2.0 m/s
   b.   1.5 m/s
   c.   1.0 m/s
   d.   2.5 m/s
   e.   3.0 m/s

38.   A 4.0-kg mass has a velocity of 4.0 m/s, east when it explodes into two 2.0-kg masses. After the explosion one of the masses has a velocity of 3.0 m/s at an angle of 60° north of east. What is the magnitude of the velocity of the other mass after the explosion?

   a.   7.9 m/s
   b.   8.9 m/s
   c.   7.0 m/s
   d.   6.1 m/s
   e.   6.7 m/s

39.   A 4.2-kg object, initially at rest, "explodes" into three objects of equal mass. Two of these are determined to have velocities of equal magnitudes (5.0 m/s) with directions that differ by 90°. How much kinetic energy was released in the explosion?

   a.   70 J
   b.   53 J
   c.   60 J
   d.   64 J
   e.   35 J

40.   A 4.0-kg mass, initially at rest on a horizontal frictionless surface, is struck by a 2.0-kg mass moving along the x axis with a speed of 8.0 m/s. After the collision, the 2.0-kg mass has a speed of 4.0 m/s at an angle of 37° from the positive x axis. What is the speed of the 4.0-kg mass after the collision?

   a.   2.0 m/s
   b.   2.7 m/s
   c.   4.9 m/s
   d.   2.4 m/s
   e.   3.6 m/s

41.   At an instant when a particle of mass 50 g has an acceleration of 80 m/s² in the positive x direction, a 75-g particle has an acceleration of 40 m/s² in the positive y direction. What is the magnitude of the acceleration of the center of mass of this two-particle system at this instant?

   a.   60 m/s²
   b.   56 m/s²
   c.   40 m/s²
   d.   50 m/s²
   e.   46 m/s²

42.   At an instant when a particle of mass 80 g has a velocity of 25 m/s in the positive y direction, a 75-g particle has a velocity of 20 m/s in the positive x direction. What is the speed of the center of mass of this two-particle system at this instant?

   a.   16 m/s
   b.   45 m/s
   c.   23 m/s
   d.   20 m/s
   e.   36 m/s

43.   Three particles are placed in the xy plane. A 40-g particle is located at (3, 4) m, and a 50-g particle is positioned at (–2, –6) m. Where must a 20-g particle be placed so that the center of mass of this three-particle system is located at the origin?

   a.   (–1, –3) m
   b.   (–1, 2) m
   c.   (–1, 12) m
   d.   (–1, 7) m
   e.   (–1, 3) m

44.   A rocket engine consumes 450 kg of fuel per minute. If the exhaust speed of the ejected fuel is 5.2 km/s, what is the thrust of the rocket?

   a.   42 kN
   b.   39 kN
   c.   45 kN
   d.   48 kN
   e.   35 kN

45.   A rocket with an initial mass of 1000 kg adjusts its thrust by varying the rate at which mass is ejected. The ejection speed relative to the rocket is 40 km/s. If the acceleration of the rocket is to have a magnitude of 20 m/s² at an instant when its mass is 80% of the original mass, at what rate is mass being ejected at that instant? Ignore any external forces on the rocket.

   a.   0.40 kg/s
   b.   0.50 kg/s
   c.   0.60 kg/s
   d.   0.70 kg/s
   e.   0.80 kg/s

46.   A rocket moving in outer space maintains a constant acceleration (magnitude = 20 m/s²) while ejecting fuel at a speed of 15 km/s relative to the rocket. If the initial mass of the rocket is 3000 kg, what is the magnitude of the thrust after 800 kg of fuel have been consumed?

   a.   56 kN
   b.   48 kN
   c.   52 kN
   d.   44 kN
   e.   36 kN

47.   Three particles are placed in the xy plane. A 30-g particle is located at (3, 4) m, and a 40-g particle is located at (–2, –2) m. Where must a 20-g particle be placed so that the center of mass of the three-particle system is at the origin?

   a.   (–3, –1) m
   b.   (+1, +3) m
   c.   (+3, –1) m
   d.   (–1, –3) m
   e.   (–0.5, –2) m

48.   At the instant a 2.0-kg particle has a velocity of 4.0 m/s in the positive x direction, a 3.0-kg particle has a velocity of 5.0 m/s in the positive y direction. What is the speed of the center of mass of the two-particle system?

   a.   3.8 m/s
   b.   3.4 m/s
   c.   5.0 m/s
   d.   4.4 m/s
   e.   4.6 m/s

49.   Two 0.20 kg balls moving at 4 m/s, East strike a wall. Ball A bounces backwards at the same speed. Ball B stops. Which statement correctly describes the change in momentum of the two balls?

a. $|\Delta p_B| < |\Delta p_A|$.
b. $|\Delta p_B| = |\Delta p_A|$.
c. $|\Delta p_B| > |\Delta p_A|$.
d. $\Delta p_B = \Delta p_A$.
e. $\Delta p_B > \Delta p_A$.

50.   Two bodies with masses m_1 and m_2 are both moving east with velocities of magnitudes v_1 and v_2, where v_1 is less than v_2. The magnitude of the velocity of the center of mass of this system of two bodies is

a.   less than v_1.
b.   equal to v_1.
c.   equal to the average of v_1 and v_2.
d.   greater than v_1 and less than v_2.
e.   greater than v_2.

51.   A car of mass m_1 traveling at velocity v passes a car of mass m_2 parked at the side of the road. The momentum of the system of two cars is

a.   0.
b. $m_1 v$.
c. $(m_1 - m_2)v$.
d. $\dfrac{m_1 v}{m_1 + m_2}$
e. $(m_1 + m_2)v$.

52.   Car A rear ends Car B, which has twice the mass of A, on an icy road at a speed low enough so that the collision is essentially elastic. Car B is stopped at a light when it is struck. Car A has mass m and speed v before the collision. After the collision

a.   each car has half the momentum.
b.   car A stops and car B has momentum mv.
c.   car A stops and car B has momentum $2mv$.
d.   the momentum of car B is four times as great in magnitude as that of car A.
e.   each car has half of the kinetic energy.

53. A 3.00 kg stone is dropped from a 39.2 m high building. When the stone has fallen 19.6 m, the magnitude of the impulse it has received from the gravitational force is

a. $9.8 \, \text{N} \cdot \text{s}$.
b. $19.6 \, \text{N} \cdot \text{s}$.
c. $29.4 \, \text{N} \cdot \text{s}$.
d. $58.8 \, \text{N} \cdot \text{s}$.
e. $117.6 \, \text{N} \cdot \text{s}$.

54. A 3.00 kg stone is dropped from a 39.2 m high building. When the stone has fallen 19.6 m, the magnitude of the impulse the Earth has received from the gravitational force exerted by the stone is

a. $9.8 \, \text{N} \cdot \text{s}$.
b. $19.6 \, \text{N} \cdot \text{s}$.
c. $29.4 \, \text{N} \cdot \text{s}$.
d. $58.8 \, \text{N} \cdot \text{s}$.
e. $117.6 \, \text{N} \cdot \text{s}$.

55. Assume that the average mass of each of the approximately 1 billion people in China is 55 kg. Assume that they all gather in one place and climb to the top of 2 m high ladders. The center of mass of the Earth is then displaced

a.   0 m.
b. 1.84×10^{-23} m.
c. 1.84×10^{-14} m.
d. 1.80×10^{-13} m.
e.   2 m.

56. A 0.28 kg stone you throw rises 34.3 m in the air. The magnitude of the impulse the stone received from your hand while being thrown is

a. $0.27 \, \text{N} \cdot \text{s}$.
b. $2.7 \, \text{N} \cdot \text{s}$.
c. $7.3 \, \text{N} \cdot \text{s}$.
d. $9.6 \, \text{N} \cdot \text{s}$.
e. $34.3 \, \text{N} \cdot \text{s}$.

57. A 0.28 kg stone you throw rises 34.3 m in the air. The impulse your hand receives from the stone while it throws the stone is

a. $2.7 \, \text{N} \cdot \text{s}$, up.
b. $2.7 \, \text{N} \cdot \text{s}$, down.
c. $7.3 \, \text{N} \cdot \text{s}$, up.
d. $7.3 \, \text{N} \cdot \text{s}$, down.
e. $9.6 \, \text{N} \cdot \text{s}$, up.

58.   A 0.28 kg stone you throw rises 34.3 m in the air. The impulse the stone receives from your hand while being thrown is

    a. $2.7\,\text{N·s}$, up.
    b. $2.7\,\text{N·s}$, down.
    c. $7.3\,\text{N·s}$, up.
    d. $7.3\,\text{N·s}$, down.
    e. $9.6\,\text{N·s}$, up.

59.   A catapult fires an 800-kg rock with an initial velocity of 100 m/s at a 40° angle to the ground. The magnitude of the horizontal impulse the catapult receives from the rock is

    a. $5.1\times10^{4}\,\text{N·s}$.
    b. $6.1\times10^{4}\,\text{N·s}$.
    c. $8.0\times10^{4}\,\text{N·s}$.
    d. $5.0\times10^{5}\,\text{N·s}$.
    e. $6.0\times10^{5}\,\text{N·s}$.

60.   A catapult fires an 800-kg rock with an initial velocity of 100 m/s at a 40° angle to the ground. The magnitude of the vertical impulse the catapult receives from the rock is

    a. $5.1\times10^{4}\,\text{N·s}$.
    b. $6.1\times10^{4}\,\text{N·s}$.
    c. $8.0\times10^{4}\,\text{N·s}$.
    d. $5.0\times10^{5}\,\text{N·s}$.
    e. $6.0\times10^{5}\,\text{N·s}$.

61.   A ball falls to the ground from height h and bounces to height h'. Momentum is conserved in the ball-earth system

    a.   no matter what height h' it reaches.
    b.   only if $h' < h$.
    c.   only if $h' = h$.
    d.   only if $h' > h$.
    e.   only if $h' \geq h$.

62.   The law of conservation of momentum applies to a collision between two bodies if

    a.   they exert equal and opposite forces on each other.
    b.   they exert forces on each other respectively proportional to their masses.
    c.   they exert forces on each other respectively proportional to their velocities.
    d.   they exert forces on each other respectively inversely proportional to their masses.
    e.   their accelerations are proportional to their masses.

63.   When two bodies of different masses collide, the impulses they exert on each other are

   a.   equal for all collisions.
   b.   equal but opposite for all collisions.
   c.   equal but opposite only for elastic collisions.
   d.   equal but opposite only for inelastic collisions.
   e.   equal but opposite only when the bodies have equal but opposite accelerations.

64.   If you know the impulse that has acted on a body of mass m you can calculate

   a.   its initial velocity.
   b.   its final velocity.
   c.   its final momentum.
   d.   the change in its velocity.
   e.   its acceleration during the impulse.

65.   Two boys in a canoe toss a baseball back and forth. What effect will this have on the canoe? Neglect (velocity-dependent) frictional forces with water or air.

   a.   None, because the ball remains in the canoe.
   b.   The canoe will drift in the direction of the boy who throws the ball harder each time.
   c.   The canoe will drift in the direction of the boy who throws the ball with less force each time.
   d.   The canoe will oscillate back and forth always moving opposite to the ball.
   e.   The canoe will oscillate in the direction of the ball because the canoe and ball exert forces in opposite directions upon the person throwing the ball.

66.   An astronaut outside a spaceship hammers a loose rivet back in place. What happens to the astronaut as he swings the hammer?

   a.   Nothing. The spaceship takes up the momentum of the hammer.
   b.   He moves away from the spaceship.
   c.   He moves towards the spaceship.
   d.   He moves towards the spaceship as he pulls the hammer back and moves away from it as he swings the hammer forward.
   e.   He moves away from the spaceship as he pulls the hammer back and moves toward it as he swings the hammer forward.

67.   The value of the momentum of a system is the same at a later time as at an earlier time if there are no

   a.   collisions between particles within the system.
   b.   inelastic collisions between particles within the system.
   c.   changes of momentum of individual particles within the system.
   d.   internal forces acting between particles within the system.
   e.   external forces acting on particles of the system.

68.   When the rate of burn and the exhaust velocity are constant, a rocket ascends with

    a.   decreasing acceleration.
    b.   decreasing velocity.
    c.   constant velocity.
    d.   constant acceleration.
    e.   increasing acceleration.

69.   Two cars start at the same point, but travel in opposite directions on a circular path of radius R, each at speed v. While each car travels a distance less than $\frac{\pi}{2}R$, one quarter circle, the center of mass of the two cars

    a.   remains at the initial point.
    b.   travels along a diameter of the circle at speed $v' < v$.
    c.   travels along a diameter of the circle at speed $v' = v$.
    d.   travels along a diameter of the circle at speed $v' > v$.
    e.   remains at the center of the circle.

Open-Ended Problems

70.   A child bounces a 50-gram superball on the sidewalk. The velocity of the superball changes from 21 m/s downward to 19 m/s upward. If the contact time with the sidewalk is 1/800 s, what is the magnitude of the force exerted on the superball by the sidewalk?

71.   High-speed stroboscopic photographs show that the head of a golf club of mass 200 grams is traveling at 55 m/s just before it strikes a 46-gram golf ball at rest on a tee. After the collision, the clubhead travels (in the same direction) at 40 m/s. Find the speed of the golf ball just after impact.

72.   A pitcher claims he can throw a baseball with as much momentum as a 3.00-g bullet moving with a speed of 1500 m/s. A baseball has a mass of 0.145 kg. What must be its speed if the pitcher's claim is valid?

73.   A U-238 nucleus (mass = 238 units) decays, transforming into an alpha particle (mass = 4 units) and a residual thorium nucleus (mass = 234 units). If the uranium nucleus was at rest, and the alpha particle has a speed of 1.5×10^7 m/s, determine the recoil speed of the thorium nucleus.

Chapter 9

Linear Momentum and Collisions

1.	c		30.	b
2.	b		31.	c
3.	b		32.	c
4.	c		33.	b
5.	a		34.	c
6.	b		35.	a
7.	b		36.	b
8.	a		37.	d
9.	c		38.	c
10.	d		39.	a
11.	b		40.	b
12.	c		41.	c
13.	d		42.	a
14.	b		43.	d
15.	d		44.	b
16.	a		45.	a
17.	a		46.	d
18.	b		47.	e
19.	c		48.	b
20.	d		49.	a
21.	a		50.	d
22.	b		51.	b
23.	c		52.	d
24.	b		53.	d
25.	d		54.	d
26.	b		55.	c
27.	a		56.	c
28.	a		57.	d
29.	d		58.	c

59.   b

60.   a

61.   a

62.   a

63.   b

64.   d

65.   d

66.   d

67.   e

68.   e

69.   b

70.   1600 N

71.   65.2 m/s

72.   31.0 m/s

73. 2.56×10^5 m/s

Chapter 10

Rotation of a Rigid Object About a Fixed Axis

Multiple Choice

1. At $t = 0$, a wheel rotating about a fixed axis at a constant angular acceleration has an angular velocity of 2.0 rad/s. Two seconds later it has turned through 5.0 complete revolutions. What is the angular acceleration of this wheel?

    a. 17 rad/s^2
    b. 14 rad/s^2
    c. 20 rad/s^2
    d. 23 rad/s^2
    e. 13 rad/s^2

2. At $t = 0$, a wheel rotating about a fixed axis at a constant angular acceleration of -0.40 rad/s^2 has an angular velocity of 1.5 rad/s and an angular position of 2.3 rad. What is the angular position of the wheel at $t = 2.0$ s?

    a. 4.9 rad
    b. 4.7 rad
    c. 4.5 rad
    d. 4.3 rad
    e. 4.1 rad

3. A wheel rotating about a fixed axis has an angular position given by $\theta = 3.0 - 2.0t^3$, where θ is measured in radians and t in seconds. What is the angular acceleration of the wheel at $t = 2.0$ s?

    a. -1.0 rad/s^2
    b. -24 rad/s^2
    c. -2.0 rad/s^2
    d. -4.0 rad/s^2
    e. -3.5 rad/s^2

4. A wheel rotating about a fixed axis with a constant angular acceleration of 2.0 rad/s^2 turns through 2.4 revolutions during a 2.0-s time interval. What is the angular velocity at the end of this time interval?

    a. 9.5 rad/s
    b. 9.7 rad/s
    c. 9.3 rad/s
    d. 9.1 rad/s
    e. 8.8 rad/s

5.   The turntable of a record player has an angular velocity of 8.0 rad/s when it is
        turned off. The turntable comes to rest 2.5 s after being turned off. Through how
        many radians does the turntable rotate after being turned off? Assume constant
        angular acceleration.

        a.   12 rad
        b.   8.0 rad
        c.   10 rad
        d.   16 rad
        e.   6.8 rad

6.   A wheel rotates about a fixed axis with an initial angular velocity of 20 rad/s.
        During a 5.0-s interval the angular velocity increases to 40 rad/s. Assume that
        the angular acceleration was constant during the 5.0-s interval. How many
        revolutions does the wheel turn through during the 5.0-s interval?

        a.   20 rev
        b.   24 rev
        c.   32 rev
        d.   28 rev
        e.   39 rev

7.   A wheel rotates about a fixed axis with an initial angular velocity of 20 rad/s.
        During a 5.0-s interval the angular velocity decreases to 10 rad/s. Assume that
        the angular acceleration is constant during the 5.0-s interval. How many radians
        does the wheel turn through during the 5.0-s interval?

        a.   95 rad
        b.   85 rad
        c.   65 rad
        d.   75 rad
        e.   125 rad

8.   A wheel starts from rest and rotates with a constant angular acceleration about a
        fixed axis. It completes the first revolution 6.0 s after it started. How long after it
        started will the wheel complete the second revolution?

        a.   9.9 s
        b.   7.8 s
        c.   8.5 s
        d.   9.2 s
        e.   6.4 s

9.   A thin uniform rod (length = 1.2 m, mass = 2.0 kg) is pivoted about a horizontal, frictionless pin through one end of the rod. (The moment of inertia of the rod about this axis is $ML^2/3$.) The rod is released when it makes an angle of 37° with the horizontal. What is the angular acceleration of the rod at the instant it is released?

    a.   9.8 rad/s^2
    b.   7.4 rad/s^2
    c.   8.4 rad/s^2
    d.   5.9 rad/s^2
    e.   6.5 rad/s^2

10.   A wheel rotating about a fixed axis has a constant angular acceleration of 4.0 rad/s^2. In a 4.0-s interval the wheel turns through an angle of 80 radians. Assuming the wheel started from rest, how long had it been in motion at the start of the 4.0-s interval?

    a.   2.5 s
    b.   4.0 s
    c.   3.5 s
    d.   3.0 s
    e.   4.5 s

11.   A wheel rotating about a fixed axis with a constant angular acceleration of 2.0 rad/s^2 starts from rest at $t = 0$. The wheel has a diameter of 20 cm. What is the magnitude of the total linear acceleration of a point on the outer edge of the wheel at $t = 0.60$ s?

    a.   0.25 m/s^2
    b.   0.50 m/s^2
    c.   0.14 m/s^2
    d.   0.34 m/s^2
    e.   0.20 m/s^2

12.   A wheel rotates about a fixed axis with a constant angular acceleration of 4.0 rad/s^2. The diameter of the wheel is 40 cm. What is the linear speed of a point on the rim of this wheel at an instant when that point has a total linear acceleration with a magnitude of 1.2 m/s^2?

    a.   39 cm/s
    b.   42 cm/s
    c.   45 cm/s
    d.   35 cm/s
    e.   53 cm/s

13.   A disk (radius = 8.0 cm) that rotates about a fixed axis starts from rest and
accelerates at a constant rate to an angular velocity of 4.0 rad/s in 2.0 s. What is
the magnitude of the total linear acceleration of a point on the rim of the disk at
the instant when the angular velocity of the disk is 1.5 rad/s?

    a.   24 cm/s^2
    b.   16 cm/s^2
    c.   18 cm/s^2
    d.   34 cm/s^2
    e.   44 cm/s^2

14.   A mass (M_1 = 5.0 kg) is connected by a light cord to a mass (M_2 = 4.0 kg) which
slides on a smooth surface, as shown in the figure. The pulley (radius = 0.20 m)
rotates about a frictionless axle. The acceleration of M_2 is 3.5 m/s^2. What is the
moment of inertia of the pulley?

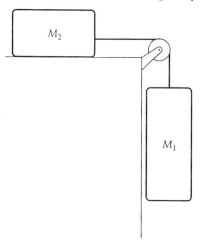

    a.   0.29 kg · m^2
    b.   0.42 kg · m^2
    c.   0.20 kg · m^2
    d.   0.62 kg · m^2
    e.   0.60 kg · m^2

15. A wheel (radius = 0.20 m) is mounted on a frictionless, horizontal axis. A light cord wrapped around the wheel supports a 0.50-kg object, as shown in the figure. When released from rest the object falls with a downward acceleration of 5.0 m/s^2. What is the moment of inertia of the wheel?

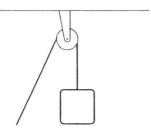

a.   0.023 kg · m^2
b.   0.027 kg · m^2
c.   0.016 kg · m^2
d.   0.019 kg · m^2
e.   0.032 kg · m^2

16. A wheel (radius = 0.25 m) is mounted on a frictionless, horizontal axis. The moment of inertia of the wheel about the axis is 0.040 kg · m^2. A light cord wrapped around the wheel supports a 0.50-kg object as shown in the figure. The object is released from rest. What is the magnitude of the acceleration of the 0.50-kg object?

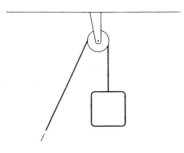

a.   3.0 m/s^2
b.   3.4 m/s^2
c.   4.3 m/s^2
d.   3.8 m/s^2
e.   2.7 m/s^2

17.   A mass $m = 4.0$ kg is connected, as shown, by a light cord to a mass $M = 6.0$ kg, which slides on a smooth horizontal surface. The pulley rotates about a frictionless axle and has a radius $R = 0.12$ m and a moment of inertia $I = 0.090$ kg · m². The cord does not slip on the pulley. What is the magnitude of the acceleration of m?

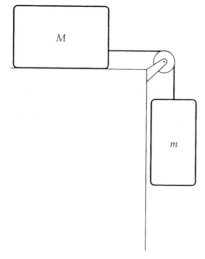

    a.   2.4 m/s²
    b.   2.8 m/s²
    c.   3.2 m/s²
    d.   4.2 m/s²
    e.   1.7 m/s²

18.   A cylinder rotating about its axis with a constant angular acceleration of 1.6 rad/s² starts from rest at $t = 0$. At the instant when it has turned through 0.40 radian, what is the magnitude of the total linear acceleration of a point on the rim (radius = 13 cm)?

    a.   0.31 m/s²
    b.   0.27 m/s²
    c.   0.35 m/s²
    d.   0.39 m/s²
    e.   0.45 m/s²

19.   A wheel (radius = 0.20 m) starts from rest and rotates with a constant angular acceleration of 2.0 rad/s². At the instant when the angular velocity is equal to 1.2 rad/s, what is the magnitude of the total linear acceleration of a point on the rim of the wheel?

    a.   0.40 m/s²
    b.   0.29 m/s²
    c.   0.69 m/s²
    d.   0.49 m/s²
    e.   0.35 m/s²

20. A horizontal disk with a radius of 10 cm rotates about a vertical axis through its center. The disk starts from rest at $t = 0$ and has a constant angular acceleration of 2.1 rad/s^2. At what value of t will the radial and tangential components of the linear acceleration of a point on the rim of the disk be equal in magnitude?

   a.   0.55 s
   b.   0.63 s
   c.   0.69 s
   d.   0.59 s
   e.   0.47 s

21. Two particles ($m_1 = 0.20$ kg, $m_2 = 0.30$ kg) are positioned at the ends of a 2.0-m long rod of negligible mass. What is the moment of inertia of this rigid body about an axis perpendicular to the rod and through the center of mass?

   a.   0.48 kg · m^2
   b.   0.50 kg · m^2
   c.   1.2 kg · m^2
   d.   0.80 kg · m^2
   e.   0.70 kg · m^2

22. Four identical particles (mass of each = 0.24 kg) are placed at the vertices of a rectangle (2.0 m × 3.0 m) and held in those positions by four light rods which form the sides of the rectangle. What is the moment of inertia of this rigid body about an axis that passes through the center of mass of the body and is parallel to the shorter sides of the rectangle?

   a.   2.4 kg · m^2
   b.   2.2 kg · m^2
   c.   1.9 kg · m^2
   d.   2.7 kg · m^2
   e.   8.6 kg · m^2

23. Four identical particles (mass of each = 0.40 kg) are placed at the vertices of a rectangle (2.5 m × 4.0 m) and held in those positions by four light rods which form the sides of the rectangle. What is the moment of inertia of this rigid body about an axis that passes through the mid-points of the shorter sides and is parallel to the longer sides?

   a.   2.2 kg · m^2
   b.   2.8 kg · m^2
   c.   2.5 kg · m^2
   d.   3.1 kg · m^2
   e.   1.6 kg · m^2

24.   Four identical particles (mass of each = 0.40 kg) are placed at the vertices of a rectangle (2.0 m × 3.0 m) and held in those positions by four light rods which form the sides of the rectangle. What is the moment of inertia of this rigid body about an axis that passes through the mid-points of the longer sides and is parallel to the shorter sides?

   a.   2.7 kg · m^2
   b.   3.6 kg · m^2
   c.   3.1 kg · m^2
   d.   4.1 kg · m^2
   e.   1.6 kg · m^2

25.   The rigid object shown is rotated about an axis perpendicular to the paper and through point P. The total kinetic energy of the object as it rotates is equal to 1.4 J. If M = 1.3 kg and L = 0.50 m, what is the angular velocity of the object? Neglect the mass of the connecting rods and treat the masses as particles.

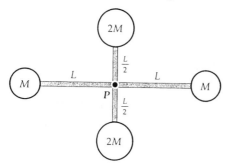

   a.   1.3 rad/s
   b.   1.5 rad/s
   c.   1.7 rad/s
   d.   1.2 rad/s
   e.   2.1 rad/s

26.   If M = 0.50 kg, L = 1.2 m, and the mass of each connecting rod shown is negligible, what is the moment of inertia about an axis perpendicular to the paper through the center of mass? Treat the mass as particles.

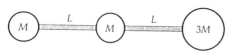

   a.   3.7 kg · m^2
   b.   2.8 kg · m^2
   c.   3.2 kg · m^2
   d.   2.3 kg · m^2
   e.   3.9 kg · m^2

27.   Three particles, each of which has a mass of 80 g, are positioned at the vertices of an equilateral triangle with sides of length 60 cm. The particles are connected by rods of negligible mass. What is the moment of inertia of this rigid body about an axis that is parallel to one side of the triangle and passes through the respective midpoints of the other two sides?

    a. $0.018 \text{ kg} \cdot \text{m}^2$
    b. $0.020 \text{ kg} \cdot \text{m}^2$
    c. $0.016 \text{ kg} \cdot \text{m}^2$
    d. $0.022 \text{ kg} \cdot \text{m}^2$
    e. $0.032 \text{ kg} \cdot \text{m}^2$

28.   A uniform rod (mass = 2.0 kg, length = 0.60 m) is free to rotate about a frictionless pivot at one end. The rod is released from rest in the horizontal position. What is the magnitude of the angular acceleration of the rod at the instant it is 60° below the horizontal?

    a. 15 rad/s^2
    b. 12 rad/s^2
    c. 18 rad/s^2
    d. 29 rad/s^2
    e. 23 rad/s^2

29.   Particles (mass of each = 0.20 kg) are placed at the 40-cm and 100-cm marks of a meter stick of negligible mass. This rigid body is free to rotate about a frictionless pivot at the 0-cm end. The body is released from rest in the horizontal position. What is the initial angular acceleration of the body?

    a. 12 rad/s^2
    b. 5.9 rad/s^2
    c. 8.4 rad/s^2
    d. 5.4 rad/s^2
    e. 17 rad/s^2

30.   Particles (mass of each = 0.40 kg) are placed at the 60-cm and 100-cm marks of a meter stick of negligible mass. This rigid body is free to rotate about a frictionless pivot at the 0-cm end. The body is released from rest in the horizontal position. What is the magnitude of the initial linear acceleration of the end of the body opposite the pivot?

    a. 15 m/s^2
    b. 9.8 m/s^2
    c. 5.8 m/s^2
    d. 12 m/s^2
    e. 4.7 m/s^2

31.   A wheel (radius = 12 cm) is mounted on a frictionless, horizontal axle that is perpendicular to the wheel and passes through the center of mass of the wheel. A light cord wrapped around the wheel supports a 0.40-kg object. If released from rest with the string taut, the object is observed to fall with a downward acceleration of 3.0 m/s². What is the moment of inertia (of the wheel) about the given axle?

    a. $0.023 \text{ kg} \cdot \text{m}^2$
    b. $0.013 \text{ kg} \cdot \text{m}^2$
    c. $0.020 \text{ kg} \cdot \text{m}^2$
    d. $0.016 \text{ kg} \cdot \text{m}^2$
    e. $0.035 \text{ kg} \cdot \text{m}^2$

32.   A uniform rod is 2.0 m long. The rod is pivoted about a horizontal, frictionless pin through one end. The rod is released from rest at an angle of 30° above the horizontal. What is the angular acceleration of the rod at the instant it is released?

    a. 4.7 rad/s^2
    b. 6.9 rad/s^2
    c. 6.4 rad/s^2
    d. 5.6 rad/s^2
    e. 4.2 rad/s^2

33.   A uniform rod is 2.0 m long. The rod is pivoted about a horizontal, frictionless pin through one end. The rod is released from rest at the horizontal position. What is the angular acceleration of the rod at the instant the rod makes an angle of 70° with the horizontal?

    a. 3.7 rad/s^2
    b. 1.3 rad/s^2
    c. 2.5 rad/s^2
    d. 4.9 rad/s^2
    e. 1.9 rad/s^2

34.   A uniform rod of mass $M = 1.2$ kg and length $L = 0.80$ m, lying on a frictionless horizontal plane, is free to pivot about a vertical axis through one end, as shown. The moment of inertia of the rod about this axis is given by ML^2. If a force ($F = 5.0$ N, $\theta = 40°$) acts as shown, what is the resulting angular acceleration about the pivot point?

Pivot

    a.   16 rad/s^2
    b.   12 rad/s^2
    c.   14 rad/s^2
    d.   10 rad/s^2
    e.   33 rad/s^2

35.   A uniform meter stick is pivoted to rotate about a horizontal axis through the 25-cm mark on the stick. The stick is released from rest in a horizontal position. The moment of inertia of a uniform rod about an axis perpendicular to the rod and through the center of mass of the rod is given by $(1/12)ML^2$. Determine the magnitude of the initial angular acceleration of the stick.

    a.   17 rad/s^2
    b.   13 rad/s^2
    c.   15 rad/s^2
    d.   19 rad/s^2
    e.   23 rad/s^2

36.   A uniform rod (length = 2.0 m) is mounted to rotate freely about a horizontal axis that is perpendicular to the rod and that passes through the rod at a point 0.50 m from one end of the rod. If the rod is released from rest in a horizontal position, what is the angular speed of the rod as it rotates through its lowest position?

    a.   3.5 rad/s
    b.   3.8 rad/s
    c.   4.1 rad/s
    d.   2.0 rad/s
    e.   5.6 rad/s

37.   Identical particles are placed at the 50-cm and 80-cm marks on a meter stick of negligible mass. This rigid body is then mounted so as to rotate freely about a pivot at the 0-cm mark on the meter stick. If this body is released from rest in a horizontal position, what is the angular speed of the meter stick as it swings through its lowest position?

   a.   4.2 rad/s
   b.   5.4 rad/s
   c.   4.6 rad/s
   d.   5.0 rad/s
   e.   1.7 rad/s

38.   A uniform rod (mass = 1.5 kg) is 2.0 m long. The rod is pivoted about a horizontal, frictionless pin through one end. The rod is released from rest in a horizontal position. What is the angular speed of the rod when the rod makes an angle of 30° with the horizontal? (The moment of inertia of the rod about the pin is 2.0 kg · m^2).

   a.   2.2 rad/s
   b.   3.6 rad/s
   c.   2.7 rad/s
   d.   3.1 rad/s
   e.   1.8 rad/s

39.   A uniform rod is 3.0 m long. The rod is pivoted about a horizontal, frictionless pin through one end. The rod is released from rest at an angle of 27° above the horizontal. What is the angular speed of the rod as it passes through the horizontal position?

   a.   3.0 rad/s
   b.   2.8 rad/s
   c.   2.1 rad/s
   d.   2.5 rad/s
   e.   3.4 rad/s

40.   A uniform rod of length (L = 2.0 m) and mass (M = 1.5 kg) is pivoted about a horizontal frictionless pin through one end. The rod is released from rest at an angle of 30° below the horizontal. What is the angular speed of the rod when it passes through the vertical position? (The moment of inertia of the rod about the pin is 2.0 kg-m^2.)

   a.   3.5 rad/s
   b.   2.7 rad/s
   c.   3.1 rad/s
   d.   2.3 rad/s
   e.   1.6 rad/s

41.   A nonuniform 2.0-kg rod is 2.0 m long. The rod is mounted to rotate freely about a horizontal axis perpendicular to the rod that passes through one end of the rod. The moment of inertia of the rod about this axis is 4.0 kg · m². The center of mass of the rod is 1.2 m from the axis. If the rod is released from rest in the horizontal position, what is its angular speed as it swings through the vertical position?

    a.   3.4 rad/s
    b.   4.4 rad/s
    c.   4.3 rad/s
    d.   5.8 rad/s
    e.   6.8 rad/s

42.   The rigid body shown rotates about an axis through its center of mass and perpendicular to the paper. If $M = 2.0$ kg and $L = 80$ cm, what is the kinetic energy of this object when its angular speed about this axis is equal to 5.0 rad/s? Neglect the mass of the connecting rod and treat the masses as particles.

    a.   18 J
    b.   15 J
    c.   12 J
    d.   23 J
    e.   26 J

43.   The rigid body shown is rotated about an axis perpendicular to the paper and through the point P. If $M = 0.40$ kg, $a = 30$ cm, and $b = 50$ cm, how much work is required to take the body from rest to an angular speed of 5.0 rad/s? Neglect the mass of the connecting rods and treat the masses as particles.

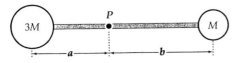

    a.   2.9 J
    b.   2.6 J
    c.   3.1 J
    d.   3.4 J
    e.   1.6 J

44.   A uniform rod (length = 2.4 m) of negligible mass has a 1.0-kg point mass attached to one end and a 2.0-kg point mass attached to the other end. The rod is mounted to rotate freely about a horizontal axis that is perpendicular to the rod and that passes through a point 1.0 m from the 2.0-kg mass. The rod is released from rest when it is horizontal. What is the angular velocity of the rod at the instant the 2.0-kg mass passes through its low point?

    a.   1.7 rad/s
    b.   2.2 rad/s
    c.   2.0 rad/s
    d.   1.5 rad/s
    e.   3.1 rad/s

45.   A campus bird spots a member of an opposing football team in an amusement park. The football player is on a ride where he goes around at angular velocity ω at distance R from the center. The bird flies in a horizontal circle above him. Will a dropping the bird releases while flying directly above the person's head hit him?

    a.   Yes, because it falls straight down.
    b.   Yes, because it maintains the acceleration of the bird as it falls.
    c.   No, because it falls straight down and will land behind the person.
    d.   Yes, because it mainatins the angular velocity of the bird as it falls.
    e.   No, because it maintains the tangential velocity the bird had at the instant it started falling.

46.   Two people are on a ride where the inside cars rotate at constant angular velocity three times the constant angular velocity of the outer cars. If the two cars are in line at $t = 0$, and moving at 3ω and ω respectively, at what time will they next pass each other?

    a. $t = 0$.

    b. $t = \dfrac{\pi}{2\omega}$.

    c. $t = \dfrac{\pi}{\omega}$.

    d. $t = \dfrac{2\pi}{\omega}$.

    e. $t = \dfrac{3\pi}{\omega}$.

47.   The figure below shows a graph of angular velocity as a function of time for a car driving around a circular track. Through how many radians does the car travel in the first 10 minutes?

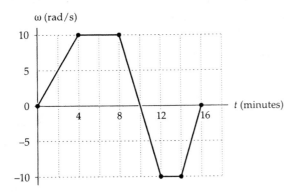

a.   30
b.   50
c.   70
d.   90
e.   100

48.   The graphs below show angular velocity as a function of time. In which one is the magnitude of the angular acceleration constantly decreasing?

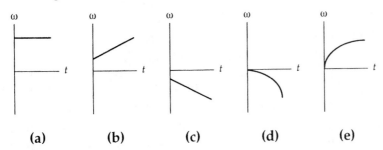

(a)   (b)   (c)   (d)   (e)

49.   You throw a Frisbee of mass m and radius r so that it is spinning about a horizontal axis perpendicular to the plane of the Frisbee. Ignoring air resistance, the torque exerted about its center of mass by gravity is

a.   0.
b. mgr.
c. $2mgr$.
d.   a function of the angular velocity.
e.   small at first, then increasing as the Frisbee loses the torque given it by your hand.

50.   Two forces of magnitude 50 N, as shown in the figure below, act on a cylinder of radius 4 m and mass 6.25 kg. The cylinder, which is initially at rest, sits on a frictionless surface. After 1 second, the velocity and angular velocity of the cylinder in m/s and rad/s are respectively

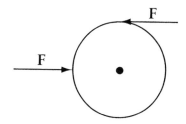

    a. $v = 0; \omega = 0.$
    b. $v = 0; \omega = 4.$
    c. $v = 0; \omega = 8.$
    d. $v = 8; \omega = 8.$
    e. $v = 16; \omega = 8.$

51.   Two cylinders made of the same material roll down a plane inclined at an angle θ with the horizontal. Each travels the same distance. The radius of cylinder B is twice the radius of cylinder A. In what order do they reach the bottom?

    a.   A reaches the bottom first because it has the greater acceleration.
    b.   A reaches the bottom first because it has a smaller moment of inertia.
    c.   B reaches the bottom first because is experiences a larger torque.
    d.   B reaches the bottom first because it travels a larger distance in one rotation.
    e.   They both reach the bottom at the same time, because each has the same linear acceleration.

52.   The figure below shows a graph of angular velocity versus time for a woman bicycling around a circular track. What is her angular displacement (in rad) in the first 8 minutes?

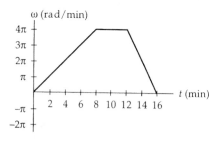

    a.   0
    b. π
    c. 4π
    d. 8π
    e. 16π

53.   The figure below shows a graph of angular velocity versus time for a woman bicycling around a circular track. What is her angular displacement (in rad) in the first 12 minutes?

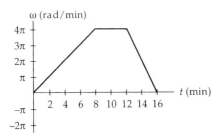

a.   0
b. 2π
c. 4π
d. 16π
e. 32π

54.   The figure below shows a graph of angular velocity versus time for a woman bicycling around a circular track. What is her angular displacement (in rad) in the 16 minute period shown in the graph?

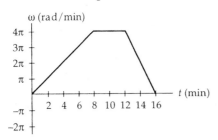

a.   0
b. 16π
c. 32π
d. 40π
e. 64π

55.   The figure below shows a graph of angular velocity versus time for a woman bicycling around a circular track. How many revolutions does she complete in the first 12 minutes?

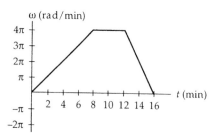

a.   4
b.   8
c.   12
d.   16
e.   32

56.   The figure below shows a graph of angular velocity versus time for a woman bicycling around a circular track. How many revolutions does she complete in the 16 minute period?

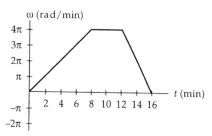

a.   8
b.   12
c.   16
d.   20
e.   40

57. A uniform sphere of radius R and mass M rotates freely about a horizontal axis that is tangent to an equatorial plane of the sphere, as shown below. The moment of inertia of the sphere about this axis is

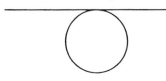

a. $\dfrac{2}{5}MR^2$.

b. $\dfrac{2}{3}MR^2$.

c. $\dfrac{5}{7}MR^2$.

d. $\dfrac{7}{5}MR^2$.

e. $\dfrac{3}{2}MR^2$.

58. A uniform cylinder of radius R, mass M, and length L rotates freely about a horizontal axis parallel and tangent to the cylinder, as shown below. The moment of inertia of the cylinder about this axis is

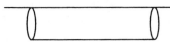

a. $\dfrac{1}{2}MR^2$.

b. $\dfrac{2}{3}MR^2$.

c. MR^2.

d. $\dfrac{3}{2}MR^2$.

e. $\dfrac{7}{5}MR^2$.

59. The angular speed of the minute hand of a clock, in rad/s, is

a. $\dfrac{1}{1800}\pi$.

b. $\dfrac{1}{60}\pi$.

c. $\dfrac{1}{30}\pi$.

d. π.

e. 120π.

60.   The angular speed of the hour hand of a clock, in rad/s, is

   a. $\dfrac{1}{7200}\pi$.

   b. $\dfrac{1}{1800}\pi$.

   c. $\dfrac{1}{30}\pi$.

   d. 1800π.

   e. 7200π.

61.   The angular speed of the hour hand of a clock, in rad/min, is

   a. $\dfrac{1}{1800}\pi$.

   b. $\dfrac{1}{60}\pi$.

   c. $\dfrac{1}{30}\pi$.

   d. π.

   e. 120π.

62.   The figure below shows a graph of angular velocity versus time for a man bicycling around a circular track. What is his average angular acceleration, in rad/s^2, in the first 10 minutes?

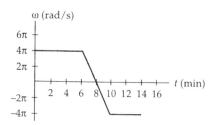

   a. 0

   b. $-\dfrac{\pi}{150}$

   c. $-\dfrac{\pi}{75}$

   d. $+\dfrac{\pi}{75}$

   e. $+\dfrac{\pi}{150}$

63.   The figure below shows a graph of angular velocity versus time for a man bicycling around a circular track. What is his average angular acceleration, in rad/s^2, in the period from $t = 6\,\text{min}$ to $t = 8\,\text{min}$?

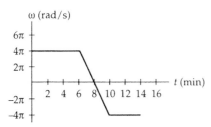

a.   0

b. $-\dfrac{\pi}{90}$

c. $-\dfrac{\pi}{30}$

d. $+\dfrac{\pi}{30}$

e. $+\dfrac{\pi}{90}$

Open-Ended Problems

64.   The net work done in accelerating a propeller from rest to an angular velocity of 200 rad/s is 3000 J. What is the moment of inertia of the propeller?

65.   A horizontal force of magnitude 6.5 N is exerted tangentially on a Frisbee of mass 32 grams and radius 14.3 cm. Assuming the Frisbee, a uniform disk, is originally at rest and the force is exerted for 0.08 s, determine the angular velocity of rotation about the central axis when the Frisbee is released.

66.   A celestial object called a pulsar emits its light in short bursts that are synchronized with its rotation. A pulsar in the Crab Nebula is rotating at a rate of 30 revolutions/second. What is the maximum radius of the pulsar, if no part of its surface can move faster than the speed of light (3×10^8 m/s)?

67.   A uniform solid sphere rolls without slipping along a horizontal surface. What fraction of its total kinetic energy is in the form of rotational kinetic energy about the CM?

Chapter 10

Rotation of a Rigid Object About a Fixed Axis

1.	b		30.	d
2.	c		31.	b
3.	b		32.	c
4.	a		33.	c
5.	c		34.	d
6.	b		35.	a
7.	d		36.	c
8.	c		37.	b
9.	a		38.	c
10.	d		39.	c
11.	a		40.	b
12.	b		41.	a
13.	a		42.	c
14.	c		43.	b
15.	d		44.	a
16.	c		45.	e
17.	a		46.	c
18.	b		47.	c
19.	d		48.	e
20.	c		49.	a
21.	a		50.	b
22.	b		51.	e
23.	c		52.	e
24.	b		53.	e
25.	c		54.	d
26.	d		55.	d
27.	c		56.	d
28.	b		57.	d
29.	a		58.	d

59.   c

60.   b

61.   c

62.   c

63.   c

64. $0.15 \, \text{kg} \cdot \text{m}^2$

65. $227 \, \text{rad/s}$

66. $1590 \, \text{km}$

67. $2/7$

Chapter 11

Angular Momentum

Multiple Choice

1. Two vectors lying in the *xy* plane are given by the equations $\mathbf{A} = 5\mathbf{i} + 2\mathbf{j}$ and $\mathbf{B} = 2\mathbf{i} - 3\mathbf{j}$. The value of $\mathbf{A} \times \mathbf{B}$ is

    a. 19k
    b. −11k
    c. −19k
    d. 11k
    e. 10i − j

2. Two vectors lying in the *xz* plane are given by the equations $\mathbf{A} = 2\mathbf{i} + 3\mathbf{k}$ and $\mathbf{B} = -\mathbf{i} + 2\mathbf{k}$. The value of $\mathbf{A} \times \mathbf{B}$ is

    a. j
    b. −j
    c. 7k
    d. −7j
    e. i + 5k

3. A particle located at the position vector $\mathbf{r} = (\mathbf{i} + \mathbf{j})$ m has a force $\mathbf{F} = (2\mathbf{i} + 3\mathbf{j})$ N acting on it. The torque about the origin is

    a. $(1\mathbf{k}) \text{N} \cdot \text{m}$
    b. $(5\mathbf{k}) \text{N} \cdot \text{m}$
    c. $(-1\mathbf{k}) \text{N} \cdot \text{m}$
    d. $(-5\mathbf{k}) \text{N} \cdot \text{m}$
    e. $(2\mathbf{i} + 3\mathbf{j}) \text{N} \cdot \text{m}$

4. A car of mass 1000 kg moves with a speed of 50 m/s on a circular track of radius 100 m. What is the magnitude of its angular momentum (in $\text{kg} \cdot \text{m}^2/\text{s}$) relative to the center of the race track?

    a. 5.0×10^2
    b. 5.0×10^6
    c. 2.5×10^4
    d. 2.5×10^6
    e. 5.0×10^3

5.   A solid cylinder of radius $R = 1.0$ m and mass 10 kg rotates about its axis. When its angular velocity is 10 rad/s, its angular momentum (in kg · m²/s) is

   a.   50.
   b.   20.
   c.   40.
   d.   25.
   e.   70.

6.   A particle whose mass is 2 kg moves in the xy plane with a constant speed of 3 m/s in the x-direction along the line $y = 5$. What is its angular momentum (in kg · m²/s) relative to the origin?

   a.   −30 k
   b.   30 k
   c.   −15 k
   d.   15 k
   e.   45 k

7.   A particle whose mass is 2 kg moves in the xy plane with a constant speed of 3 m/s along the direction $\mathbf{r} = \mathbf{i} + \mathbf{j}$. What is its angular momentum (in kg · m²/s) relative to the origin?

   a.   0 k
   b. $6\sqrt{2}$ k
   c. $-6\sqrt{2}$ k
   d.   6 k
   e.   −6 k

8.   A particle whose mass is 2.0 kg moves in the xy plane with a constant speed of 3.0 m/s along the direction $\mathbf{r} = \mathbf{i} + \mathbf{j}$. What is its angular momentum (in kg · m²/s) relative to the point $(0, 5.0)$ meters?

   a.   12 k
   b.   11 k
   c.   13 k
   d.   14 k
   e.   21 k

9.   In the figure, a 1.6-kg weight swings in a vertical circle at the end of a string having negligible weight. The string is 2 m long. If the weight is released with zero initial velocity from a horizontal position, its angular momentum (in $kg \cdot m^2/s$) at the lowest point of its path relative to the center of the circle is approximately

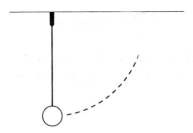

       a.   40
       b.   10
       c.   30
       d.   20
       e.   50

10.   A massless rope is wrapped around a uniform cylinder that has radius R and mass M, as shown in the figure. Initially, the unwrapped portion of the rope is vertical and the cylinder is horizontal. The linear acceleration of the cylinder is

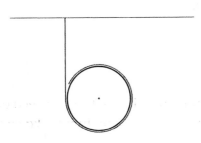

       a. $(2/3)g$
       b. $(1/2)g$
       c. $(1/3)g$
       d. $(1/6)g$
       e. $(5/6)g$

11.   Two blocks, $m_1 = 1.0$ kg and $m_2 = 2.0$ kg, are connected by a light string as shown in the figure. If the radius of the pulley is 1.0 m and its moment of inertia is 5.0 kg $\cdot$ m^2, the acceleration of the system is

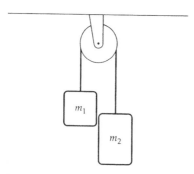

    a. $(1/6)g$
    b. $(3/8)g$
    c. $(1/8)g$
    d. $(1/2)g$
    e. $(5/8)g$

12.   A puck on a frictionless air hockey table has a mass of 5.0 kg and is attached to a cord passing through a hole in the surface as in the figure. The puck is revolving at a distance 2.0 m from the hole with an angular velocity of 3.0 rad/s. The angular momentum of the puck (in kg $\cdot$ m^2/s) is

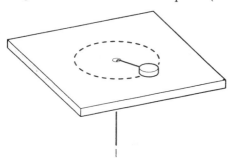

    a.   80
    b.   20
    c.   30
    d.   60
    e.   50

13.   A pendulum bob of mass m is set into motion in a circular path in a horizontal plane as shown in the figure. The square of the angular momentum of the bob about the vertical axis through the point **P** is

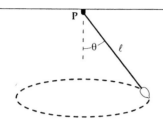

   a. $m^2 g \ell^3 \sin^4 \theta / \cos \theta$

   b. $m^2 g \ell^3 \sin^3 \theta / \cos \theta$

   c. $m^2 g \ell^3 \sin^2 \theta / \cos \theta$

   d. $m^2 g \ell^3 \sin \theta / \cos \theta$

   e. $m^2 g \ell^3 \sin^2 \theta$

14.   A puck on a frictionless air hockey table has a mass of 5.0 g and is attached to a cord passing through a hole in the surface as in the figure. The puck is revolving at a distance 2.0 m from the hole with an angular velocity of 3.0 rad/s. The cord is then pulled from below, shortening the radius to 1.0 m. The new angular velocity (in rad/s) is

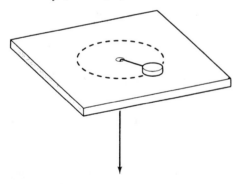

   a.   4.0

   b.   6.0

   c.   12

   d.   2.0

   e.   8.0

15.   A thin rod of mass M and length L is struck at one end by a ball of clay of mass m, moving with speed v as shown in the figure. The ball sticks to the rod. After the collision, the angular momentum of the clay-rod system about A, the midpoint of the rod, is

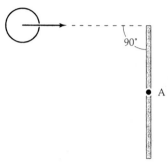

a. $(m + M/3)(vL/2)$
b. $(m + M/12)(vL/2)$
c. $(m + M/6)(vL/2)$
d. $mvL/2$
e. mvL

16.   A particle of mass $m = 0.10$ kg and speed $v_0 = 5.0$ m/s collides and sticks to the end of a uniform solid cylinder of mass $M = 1.0$ kg and radius $R = 20$ cm. If the cylinder is initially at rest and is pivoted about a frictionless axle through its center, what is the final angular velocity (in rad/s) of the system after the collision?

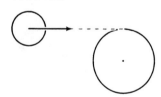

a.   8.1
b.   2.0
c.   6.1
d.   4.2
e.   10

17.   A skater extends her arms horizontally, holding a 5-kg mass in each hand. She is rotating about a vertical axis with an angular velocity of one revolution per second. If she drops her hands to her sides, what will the final angular velocity (in rev/s) be if her moment of inertia remains approximately constant at 5 kg · m^2, and the distance of the masses from the axis changes from 1 m to .1 m?

a.   6
b.   3
c.   9
d.   4
e.   7

18.   A merry-go-round of radius $R = 2.0$ m has a moment of inertia $I = 250$ kg · m²,
       and is rotating at 10 rpm. A child whose mass is 25 kg jumps onto the edge of the
       merry-go-round, heading directly toward the center at 6.0 m/s. The new angular
       speed (in rpm) of the merry-go-round is approximately

       a.   10
       b.   9.2
       c.   8.5
       d.   7.1
       e.   6.4

19.   A solid sphere (radius R, mass M) rolls without slipping down an incline as
       shown in the figure. The linear acceleration of its center of mass is

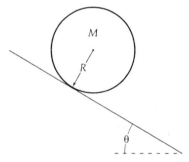

       a. $(5/7)g \sin \theta$
       b. $(3/5)g \sin \theta$
       c. $(2/3)g \sin \theta$
       d. $(1/2)g \sin \theta$
       e. $(4/5)g \sin \theta$

20.   A solid cylinder rolls without slipping down an incline as shown in the figure.
       The linear acceleration of its center of mass is

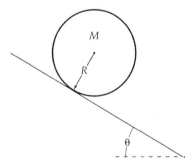

       a. $(5/7)g \sin \theta$
       b. $(1/2)g \sin \theta$
       c. $(2/3)g \sin \theta$
       d. $(3/5)g \sin \theta$
       e. $(4/5)g \sin \theta$

21.   A cylindrical shell rolls without slipping down an incline as shown in the figure. The linear acceleration of its center of mass is

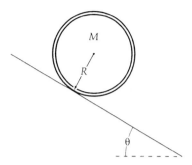

   a. $(5/7)g \sin \theta$
   b. $(1/2)g \sin \theta$
   c. $(3/5)g \sin \theta$
   d. $(2/3)g \sin \theta$
   e. $(4/5)g \sin \theta$

22.   A solid sphere, spherical shell, solid cylinder and a cylindrical shell all have the same mass m and radius R. If they are all released from rest at the same elevation and roll without slipping, which reaches the bottom of an inclined plane first?

   a.   solid sphere
   b.   spherical shell
   c.   solid cylinder
   d.   cylindrical shell
   e.   all take the same time

23.   Stars originate as large bodies of slowly rotating gas. Because of gravity, these clumps of gas slowly decrease in size. The angular velocity of a star increases as it shrinks because of

   a.   conservation of angular momentum
   b.   conservation of linear momentum
   c.   conservation of energy
   d.   the law of universal gravitation
   e.   conservation of mass

24.   Five objects of mass m move at velocity $\mathbf{v}$ at a distance r from an axis of rotation perpendicular to the page through point A, as shown below. The one that has zero angular momentum about that axis is

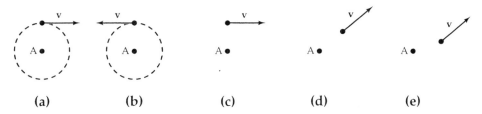

(a)   (b)   (c)   (d)   (e)

25.   The object shown below has mass m and velocity $\mathbf{v}$. The direction of its angular momentum vector with respect to an axis perpendicular to the page through point O is

O•

   a.   downwards.
   b.   to the right.
   c.   into the page.
   d.   up out of the page.
   e.   counterclockwise.

26.   Two objects of mass $m_1 = 2m$ and $m_2 = m$ move around a rotation axis O in parallel circles of radii $r_1 = r$ and $r_2 = 2r$ with equal tangential speeds. As they rotate, forces of equal magnitude are applied opposite to their velocities to stop them. Which statement is correct?

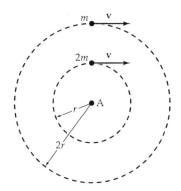

   a. m_2 will stop first because it has the larger initial angular velocity.
   b. m_1 will stop first because it has the smaller radius.
   c. m_2 will stop first because the torque on it is greater.
   d. m_1 will stop first because it has the smaller moment of inertia.
   e.   Both objects will stop at the same time because the angular accelerations are equal.

27.   A torque can be exerted on a body with a fixed axis of rotation

    a.   only by a centripetal force.

    b.   only by a force directed radially outwards.

    c.   only by a tangential force.

    d.   only by a force with a component directed radially outwards.

    e.   by any force perpendicular to but not pointing directly toward or away from the axis of rotation.

28.   Five identical cylinders are each acted on by forces of equal magnitude. Which force exerts the biggest torque?

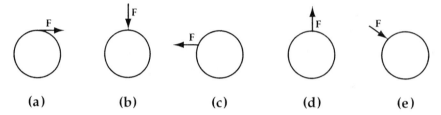

    (a)   (b)   (c)   (d)   (e)

29.   The diagram below shows five cylinders, each cylinder rotating with constant angular velocity about its central axis. The magnitude of the tangential velocity of one point of each cylinder is shown, along with each cylinder's radius and mass. Which cylinder has the largest angular momentum?

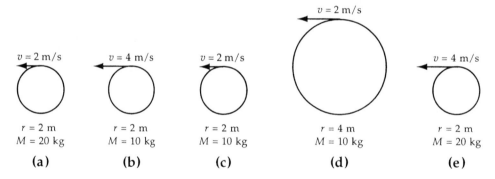

    (a)   (b)   (c)   (d)   (e)

30.   The diagram below shows five thin cylindrical shells, each shell rotating with constant angular velocity about its central axis. The magnitude of the tangential velocity of one point of each cylinder is shown, along with each cylinder's radius and mass. Which cylindrical shell has the largest angular momentum?

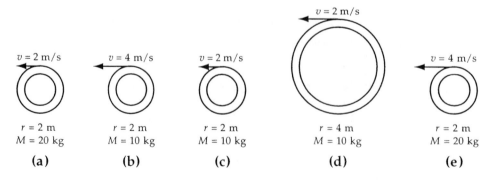

    (a)   (b)   (c)   (d)   (e)

31. The diagram below shows five 20-kg rods of the same 2.0-m length free to rotate about axes through the rods, as indicated. Which rod experiences the greatest gravitational torque?

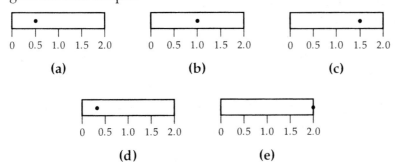

(a)   (b)   (c)

(d)   (e)

32. A force **F** is applied to a cylindrical roll of paper of radius R and mass M by pulling on the paper as shown. The acceleration of the center of mass of the roll of paper (when it rolls without slipping) is

a. $\dfrac{1}{2}\dfrac{F}{M}$.

b. $\dfrac{F}{M}$.

c. $\dfrac{3}{2}\dfrac{F}{M}$.

d. $\dfrac{4}{3}\dfrac{F}{M}$.

e. $\dfrac{2F}{M}$.

33.   A 0.5 kg fish, hooked as shown below, starts to swim away at a speed of 3 m/s. The angular momentum of the fish relative to the hand holding the fishing rod is about

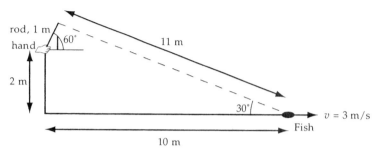

a. $3 \dfrac{\text{kg} \cdot \text{m}^2}{\text{s}}$.

b. $6 \dfrac{\text{kg} \cdot \text{m}^2}{\text{s}}$.

c. $17 \dfrac{\text{kg} \cdot \text{m}^2}{\text{s}}$.

d. $30 \dfrac{\text{kg} \cdot \text{m}^2}{\text{s}}$.

e. $60 \dfrac{\text{kg} \cdot \text{m}^2}{\text{s}}$.

Open-Ended Problems

34.   Halley's comet moves about the sun in an elliptical orbit with its closest approach to the sun being 0.59 A.U. and its furthest distance being 35 A.U. [1 Astronomical Unit (A.U.) is the Earth-sun distance]. If the comet's speed at closest approach is 54 km/s, what is its speed when it is farthest from the sun?

35.   What is the angular momentum of the moon about the Earth? The mass of the moon is 7.35×10^{22} kg, the center-to-center separation of the Earth and the moon is 3.84×10^5 km, and the orbital period of the moon is 27.3 days.

36.   A regulation basketball has a 25-cm diameter and a mass of 0.56 kg. It may be approximated as a thin spherical shell with a moment of inertia $\dfrac{2}{3}MR^2$. Starting from rest, how long will it take a basketball to roll without slipping 4.0 m down an incline at 30° to the horizontal?

37.   A coin with a diameter 3.0 cm rolls up a 30° inclined plane. The coin starts out with an initial angular speed of 60.0 rad/s and rolls in a straight line without slipping. If the moment of inertia of the coin is $\dfrac{1}{2}MR^2$, how far will the coin roll up the inclined plane?

Chapter 11
Angular Momentum

1.	c	20.	c
2.	d	21.	b
3.	a	22.	a
4.	b	23.	a
5.	a	24.	d
6.	a	25.	c
7.	a	26.	c
8.	e	27.	e
9.	d	28.	a
10.	a	29.	e
11.	c	30.	e
12.	d	31.	e
13.	a	32.	d
14.	c	33.	a
15.	d	34.	$910 \, \text{m/s}$
16.	d	35.	$2.89 \times 10^{34} \, \text{kg} \cdot \text{m}^2/\text{s}$
17.	b	36.	$1.65 \, \text{s}$
18.	d	37.	$12.4 \, \text{cm}$
19.	a		

Chapter 12

Static Equilibrium and Elasticity

Multiple Choice

1. A uniform ladder 15 ft long is leaning against a frictionless wall at an angle of 53° above the horizontal. The weight of the ladder is 30 pounds. A 75-lb boy climbs 6.0-ft up the ladder. What is the magnitude of the friction force exerted on the ladder by the floor?

    a. 43 lb
    b. 34 lb
    c. 38 lb
    d. 47 lb
    e. 24 lb

2. A horizontal meter stick supported at the 50-cm mark has a mass of 0.50 kg hanging from it at the 20-cm mark and a 0.30 kg mass hanging from it at the 60-cm mark. Determine the position on the meter stick at which one would hang a third mass of 0.60 kg to keep the meter stick balanced.

    a. 74 cm
    b. 70 cm
    c. 65 cm
    d. 86 cm
    e. 62 cm

3.   The figure shows a uniform, horizontal beam (length = 10 m, mass = 25 kg) that
        is pivoted at the wall, with its far end supported by a cable that makes an angle
        of 51° with the horizontal. If a person (mass = 60 kg) stands 3.0 m from the pivot,
        what is the tension in the cable?

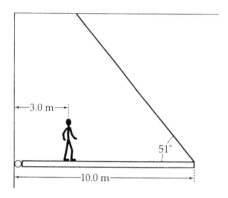

        a.   0.83 kN
        b.   0.30 kN
        c.   0.39 kN
        d.   0.42 kN
        e.   3.0 kN

4.   A uniform 100-lb beam is held in a vertical position by a pin at its lower end and
        a cable at its upper end. A horizontal force (magnitude P) acts as shown in the
        figure. If P = 75 lb, what is the tension in the cable?

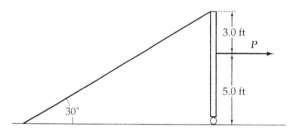

        a.   54 lb
        b.   69 lb
        c.   47 lb
        d.   61 lb
        e.   75 lb

5.   A 25-ft long crane supported at its lower end by a pin is elevated by a horizontal cable as shown in the figure. A 250-lb load is suspended from the outer end of the crane. The center of gravity of the crane is 10 ft from the pin, and the crane weighs 200 lb. What is the tension in the horizontal cable?

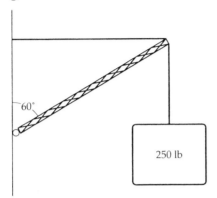

250 lb

    a.   610 lb
    b.   540 lb
    c.   640 lb
    d.   570 lb
    e.   2000 lb

6.   A uniform beam having a mass of 60 kg and a length of 2.8 m is held in place at its lower end by a pin. Its upper end leans against a vertical frictionless wall as shown in the figure. What is the magnitude of the force the pin exerts on the beam?

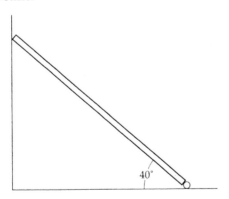

40°

    a.   0.68 kN
    b.   0.57 kN
    c.   0.74 kN
    d.   0.63 kN
    e.   0.35 kN

7.   A uniform 120-lb beam is supported in a horizontal position by a pin and cable as shown in the figure. What is the magnitude of the force by the pin on the beam?

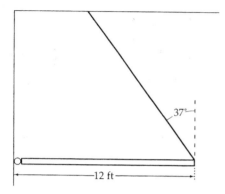

a.   94 lb
b.   88 lb
c.   63 lb
d.   75 lb
e.   150 lb

8.   A 20-m long steel wire (cross-section 1 cm², Young's modulus 2×10^{11} N/m²), is subjected to a load of 25,000 N. How much will the wire stretch under the load?

a.   0.25 cm
b.   2.5 cm
c.   12.5 cm
d.   25 cm
e.   1.25 cm

9.   How large a force is necessary to stretch a 2-mm diameter copper wire ($Y = 11 \times 10^{10}$ N/m²) by 1%?

a.   2 163 N
b.   3 455 N
c.   6 911 N
d.   11 146 N
e.   5 420 N

10.   How large a pressure increase (in ATM) must be applied to water if it is to be compressed in volume by 1%? The bulk modulus of water is 2×10^9 N/m² and 1 ATM = 10^5 N/m².

a.   50 ATM
b.   100 ATM
c.   1 080 ATM
d.   400 ATM
e.   200 ATM

11.   The diagrams below show forces applied to a wheel that weighs 20 N. The symbol **W** stands for the weight. In which diagram(s) is the wheel in equilibrium?

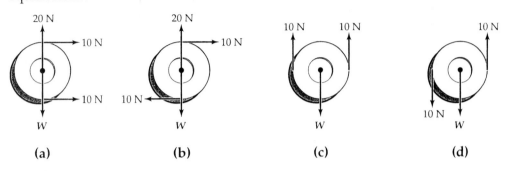

(a)   (b)   (c)   (d)

a.   A
b.   B
c.   C
d.   D
e.   A and C

12.   The diagrams below show forces of magnitude F applied to an equilateral triangular block of uniform thickness. In which diagram(s) is the block in equilibrium?

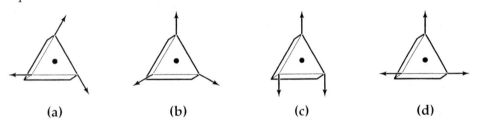

(a)   (b)   (c)   (d)

a.   A
b.   B
c.   C
d.   D
e.   A and B

13.   A square of side $\dfrac{L}{2}$ is removed from one corner of a square sandwich that has sides of length L. The center of mass of the remainder of the sandwich moves from C to C'. The displacement of the x coordinate of the center of mass (from C to C') is

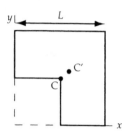

a. $\dfrac{1}{12}L$.

b. $\dfrac{\sqrt{2}}{12}L$.

c. $\dfrac{1}{6}L$.

d. $\dfrac{1}{8}L$.

e. $\dfrac{\sqrt{2}}{8}L$.

14.   A square of side $\dfrac{L}{2}$ is removed from one corner of a square sandwich that has

sides of length L. The center of mass of the remainder of the sandwich moves
from C to C′. The displacement of the y coordinate of the center of mass (from C
to C′) is

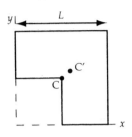

a. $\dfrac{1}{12}L$.

b. $\dfrac{\sqrt{2}}{12}L$.

c. $\dfrac{1}{6}L$.

d. $\dfrac{1}{8}L$.

e. $\dfrac{\sqrt{2}}{8}L$.

15.   A square of side $\dfrac{L}{2}$ is removed from one corner of a square sandwich that has

sides of length L. The center of mass of the remainder of the sandwich moves
from C to C′. The distance from C to C′ is

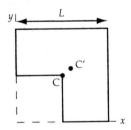

a. $\dfrac{1}{12}L$.

b. $\dfrac{\sqrt{2}}{12}L$.

c. $\dfrac{1}{6}L$.

d. $\dfrac{1}{8}L$.

e. $\dfrac{\sqrt{2}}{8}L$.

16.   Which one of the following cannot be a definition of an elastic modulus?

a. $-V_i \dfrac{\Delta P}{\Delta V}$

b. $\dfrac{Fh}{A\Delta x}$

c. $\dfrac{FL_i}{A\Delta L}$

d. $V_i \dfrac{\Delta V}{\Delta P}$

e. $\dfrac{\text{stress}}{\text{strain}}$

17.   One of the curators at the art museum is tilting a large cylinder backward. At what angle θ will the cylinder of height h and radius r be in unstable equilibrium?

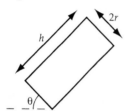

a. $\theta = \sin^{-1}\left(\dfrac{2r}{h}\right).$

b. $\theta = \cos^{-1}\left(\dfrac{2r}{h}\right).$

c. $\theta = \tan^{-1}\left(\dfrac{2r}{h}\right).$

d. $\theta = \sin^{-1}\left(\dfrac{r}{h}\right).$

e. $\theta = \tan^{-1}\left(\dfrac{r}{h}\right).$

18.   Pairs of forces of equal magnitude act on identical cylinders as shown in the figures. In which example is the cylinder in translational and rotational equilibrium?

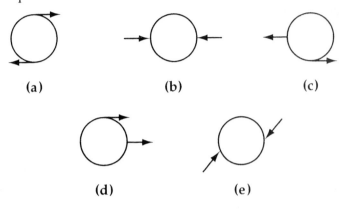

(a)   (b)   (c)

(d)   (e)

Open-Ended Problems

19.   For safety in climbing, a mountaineer uses a 50-m long nylon rope that is 1.0 cm in diameter. When supporting a 90-kg climber, the rope elongates 1.6 m. Find the Young's modulus for the rope material.

20.   The four tires of an automobile are inflated to a gauge pressure of 2.0×10^5 N/m^2 (29 PSI). Each of the four tires has an area of 0.024 m^2 that is in contact with the ground. Determine the weight of the auto.

21.   Find the minimum diameter of a steel wire 18 m long that will stretch no more than 9 mm when a load of 380 kg is hung on the lower end.
       ($Y_{steel} = 2.0 \times 10^{11}$ N/m^2).

22.   If 1.0 m^3 of concrete weighs 5×10^4 N, what is the height of the tallest cylindrical concrete pillar that will not collapse under its own weight? (The compression strength of concrete is 1.7×10^7 N/m^2)

Chapter 12

Static Equilibrium and Elasticity

1.	b	13.	a
2.	b	14.	a
3.	c	15.	b
4.	a	16.	d
5.	d	17.	c
6.	a	18.	b
7.	d	19.	$3.51 \times 10^8 \, \text{N/m}^2$
8.	b	20.	19 200 N
9.	b	21.	6.89 mm
10.	e	22.	340 m
11.	c		
12.	b		

Chapter 13

Universal Gravitation

Multiple Choice

1.   A satellite circles planet Roton every 2.8 h in an orbit having a radius of 1.2×10^7 m. If the radius of Roton is 5.0×10^6 m, what is the magnitude of the free-fall acceleration on the surface of Roton?

   a.   31 m/s^2
   b.   27 m/s^2
   c.   34 m/s^2
   d.   40 m/s^2
   e.   19 m/s^2

2.   The period of a satellite circling planet Nutron is observed to be 84 s when it is in a circular orbit with a radius of 8.0×10^6 m. What is the mass of planet Nutron?

   a. 6.2×10^{28} kg
   b. 5.0×10^{28} kg
   c. 5.5×10^{28} kg
   d. 4.3×10^{28} kg
   e. 3.7×10^{28} kg

3.   A 50-kg satellite circles planet Cruton every 5.6 h in an orbit with a radius of 12×10^6 m. What is the magnitude of the gravitational force on the satellite by planet Cruton?

   a.   63 N
   b.   58 N
   c.   68 N
   d.   73 N
   e.   50 N

4.   Two stars of masses M and $6M$ are separated by a distance D. Determine the distance (measured from M) to a point at which the net gravitational force on a third mass would be zero.

   a.   0.41 D
   b.   0.33 D
   c.   0.37 D
   d.   0.29 D
   e.   0.14 D

5.   What is the magnitude of the free-fall acceleration at a point that is a distance $2R$ above the surface of the Earth, where R is the radius of the Earth?

    a. 4.8 m/s^2
    b. 1.1 m/s^2
    c. 3.3 m/s^2
    d. 2.5 m/s^2
    e. 6.5 m/s^2

6.   A satellite is in a circular orbit about the Earth at an altitude at which air resistance is negligible. Which of the following statements is true?

    a.   There is only one force acting on the satellite.
    b.   There are two forces acting on the satellite, and their resultant is zero.
    c.   There are two forces acting on the satellite, and their resultant is not zero.
    d.   There are three forces acting on the satellite.
    e.   None of the preceding statements are correct.

7.   Three 5.0-kg masses are located at points in the xy plane as shown in the figure. What is the magnitude of the resultant force (caused by the other two masses) on the mass at the origin?

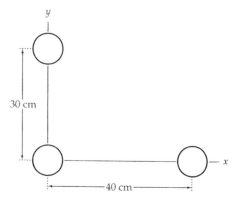

    a. $2.7 \times 10^{-8} \text{ N}$
    b. $2.1 \times 10^{-8} \text{ N}$
    c. $1.8 \times 10^{-8} \text{ N}$
    d. $2.4 \times 10^{-8} \text{ N}$
    e. $2.9 \times 10^{-8} \text{ N}$

8.   Three 5.0-kg masses are located at points in the *xy* plane, as shown. What is the magnitude of the resultant force (caused by the other two masses) on the mass at $x = 0.40$ m, $y = 0$?

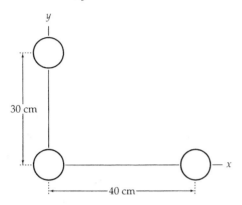

a. 2.2×10^{-8} N
b. 1.9×10^{-8} N
c. 1.4×10^{-8} N
d. 1.6×10^{-8} N
e. 2.5×10^{-8} N

9.   Three 5.0-kg masses are located at points in the *xy* plane, as shown. What is the magnitude of the resultant force (caused by the other two masses) on the mass at $x = 0$, $y = 0.30$ m?

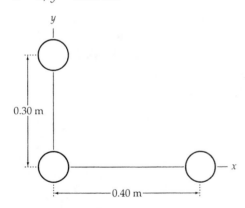

a. 2.6×10^{-8} N
b. 2.0×10^{-8} N
c. 2.9×10^{-8} N
d. 2.3×10^{-8} N
e. 2.1×10^{-8} N

10.   What is the gravitational force on a 20-kg satellite circling the Earth
(radius = 6.4×10^6 m, mass = 6.0×10^{24} kg) with a period of 5.0 h?

    a.   88 N
    b.   55 N
    c.   36 N
    d.   98 N
    e.   18 N

11.   A spaceship of mass m circles a planet (mass = M) in an orbit of radius R. How
much energy is required to transfer the spaceship to a circular orbit of radius $3R$?

    a. $GmM/(2R)$
    b. $GmM/(3R)$
    c. $GmM/(4R)$
    d. $GmM/(6R)$
    e. $3GmM/(4R)$

12.   A spacecraft (mass = m) orbits a planet (mass = M) in a circular orbit (radius = R).
What is the minimum energy required to send this spacecraft to a distant point in
space where the gravitational force on the spacecraft by the planet is negligible?

    a. $GmM/(4R)$
    b. GmM/R
    c. $GmM/(2R)$
    d. $GmM/(3R)$
    e. $2GmM/(5R)$

13.   A projectile is launched from the surface of a planet (mass = M, radius = R).
What minimum launch speed is required if the projectile is to rise to a height of
$2R$ above the surface of the planet? Disregard any dissipative effects of the
atmosphere.

    a. $\left[\dfrac{4GM}{3R}\right]^{1/2}$

    b. $\left[\dfrac{8GM}{5R}\right]^{1/2}$

    c. $\left[\dfrac{3GM}{2R}\right]^{1/2}$

    d. $\left[\dfrac{5GM}{3R}\right]^{1/2}$

    e. $\left[\dfrac{GM}{3R}\right]^{1/2}$

14. An object is released from rest at a distance h above the surface of a planet (mass = M, radius = $R < h$). With what speed will the object strike the surface of the planet? Disregard any dissipative effects of the atmosphere of the planet.

a. $\left[\dfrac{2GMh}{R(R+h)}\right]^{1/2}$

b. $\left[\dfrac{2GM}{R}\right]^{1/2}$

c. $\left[\dfrac{2GM(h-R)}{Rh}\right]^{1/2}$

d. $\left[\dfrac{2GM}{R+h}\right]^{1/2}$

e. $\left[\dfrac{2GM}{R+h}\right]^{1/2}$

15. What is the kinetic energy of a 200-kg satellite as it follows a circular orbit of radius 8.0×10^6 m around the Earth? (Mass of Earth = 6.0×10^{24} kg.)

a. 5.0×10^9 J
b. 1.0×10^{10} J
c. 1.5×10^{10} J
d. 2.0×10^{10} J
e. 2.5×10^9 J

16. An object is released from rest when it is a height h above the surface of a planet of mass M and radius R. What is the speed of the object just before striking the surface of the planet? Neglect any air resistance. Let $h = 4.0 \times 10^6$ m, $R = 5.0 \times 10^6$ m, and $M = 4.0 \times 10^{24}$ kg.

a. 7.8 km/s
b. 3.5 km/s
c. 5.4 km/s
d. 6.9 km/s
e. 4.8 km/s

17. A 50-kg satellite circles the Earth in an orbit with a period of 120 min. What minimum energy is required to change the orbit to another circular orbit with a period of 180 min? (Earth: radius = 6.4×10^6 m, mass = 6.0×10^{24} kg)

a. 2.9×10^8 J
b. 3.5×10^8 J
c. 4.1×10^8 J
d. 4.7×10^8 J
e. 5.9×10^8 J

18. Planet Roton has a mass of 4.0×10^{23} kg and a radius of 2.0×10^6 m. With what speed should a space probe be launched from the surface of Roton so as to achieve a maximum distance of 3.0×10^6 m from the center of Roton?

    a.   4.2 km/s
    b.   3.9 km/s
    c.   3.0 km/s
    d.   3.4 km/s
    e.   6.0 km/s

19. Planet Zero has a mass of 5.0×10^{23} kg and a radius of 2.0×10^6 m. A space probe is launched vertically from the surface of Zero with an initial speed of 4.0 km/s. What is the speed of the probe when it is 3.0×10^6 m from Zero's center?

    a.   3.0 km/s
    b.   2.2 km/s
    c.   1.6 km/s
    d.   3.7 km/s
    e.   5.9 km/s

20. What is the escape speed from a planet of mass M and radius R if $M = 3.2 \times 10^{23}$ kg and $R = 2.4 \times 10^6$ m?

    a.   5.5 km/s
    b.   4.2 km/s
    c.   5.2 km/s
    d.   4.8 km/s
    e.   3.7 km/s

21. A satellite of mass m circles a planet of mass M and radius R in an orbit at a height $2R$ above the surface of the planet. What minimum energy is required to change the orbit to one for which the height of the satellite is $3R$ above the surface of the planet?

    a. $\dfrac{GmM}{24R}$

    b. $\dfrac{GmM}{15R}$

    c. $\dfrac{GmM}{12R}$

    d. $\dfrac{2GmM}{21R}$

    e. $\dfrac{3GmM}{5R}$

22.   Planet Zero has a mass of 4.0×10^{23} kg and a radius of 2.0×10^6 m. A 10-kg space probe is launched vertically from the surface of Zero with an initial kinetic energy of 8.0×10^7 J. What maximum distance from the center of Zero is achieved by the probe?

a. 3.2×10^6 m
b. 4.0×10^6 m
c. 6.0×10^6 m
d. 5.0×10^6 m
e. 2.5×10^6 m

23.   Two satellites are placed in geosynchronous orbits, orbits with a period of 24 hours, where each satellite hovers over a spot on the Earth's equator. Satellite B has three times the mass of satellite A. What is the relationship between the magnitudes of the gravitational forces of the Earth on the two satellites?

a. $F_B = \dfrac{1}{9} F_A$.

b. $F_B = \dfrac{1}{3} F_A$.

c. $F_B = F_A$.
d. $F_B = 3F_A$.
e. $F_B = 9F_A$.

24.   A satellite is placed in a geosynchronous orbit. In this equatorial orbit with a period of 24 hours, the satellite hovers over one point on the equator. Which statement is true for a satellite in such an orbit?

a.   There is no gravitational force on the satellite.
b.   There is no acceleration toward the center of the Earth.
c.   The satellite is in a state of free fall toward the Earth.
d.   There is a tangential force that helps the satellite keep up with the rotation of the Earth.
e.   The force toward the center of the Earth is balanced by a force away from the center of the Earth.

25.   Two identical planets orbit a star in concentric circular orbits in the star's equatorial plane. Of the two, the planet that is farther from the star must have

a.   the smaller period.
b.   the greater period.
c.   the smaller gravitational mass.
d.   the larger gravitational mass.
e.   the larger universal gravitational constant.

26.   Which of the following quantities is conserved for a planet orbiting a star in a circular orbit? Only the planet itself is to be taken as the system; the star is not included.

   a.   Momentum and energy.
   b.   Energy and angular momentum.
   c.   Momentum and angular momentum.
   d.   Momentum, angular momentum and energy.
   e.   None of the above.

27.   The figure below shows a planet traveling in a counterclockwise direction on an elliptical path around a star located at one focus of the ellipse. When the planet is at point A,

   a.   its speed is constant.
   b.   its speed is increasing.
   c.   its speed is decreasing.
   d.   its speed is a maximum.
   e.   its speed is a minimum.

28.   The figure below shows a planet traveling in a clockwise direction on an elliptical path around a star located at one focus of the ellipse. When the planet is at point A,

   a.   its speed is constant.
   b.   its speed is increasing.
   c.   its speed is decreasing.
   d.   its speed is a maximum.
   e.   its speed is a minimum.

29.   The figure below shows a planet traveling in a counterclockwise direction on an elliptical path around a star located at one focus of the ellipse. When the planet is at point A,

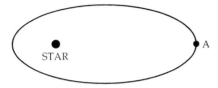

    a.   its speed is constant.
    b.   its speed is increasing.
    c.   its speed is decreasing.
    d.   its speed is a maximum.
    e.   its speed is a minimum.

30.   The figure below shows a planet traveling in a counterclockwise direction on an elliptical path around a star located at one focus of the ellipse. When the planet is at point A,

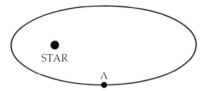

    a.   its speed is constant.
    b.   its speed is increasing.
    c.   its speed is decreasing.
    d.   its speed is a maximum.
    e.   its speed is a minimum.

31.   The figure below shows a planet traveling in a clockwise direction on an elliptical path around a star located at one focus of the ellipse. When the planet is at point A,

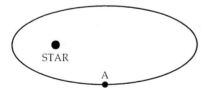

    a.   its speed is constant.
    b.   its speed is increasing.
    c.   its speed is decreasing.
    d.   its speed is a maximum.
    e.   its speed is a minimum.

32. The figure below shows a planet traveling in a counterclockwise direction on an elliptical path around a star located at one focus of the ellipse. When the planet is at point A,

    a.   its speed is decreasing.
    b.   its angular momentum is increasing.
    c.   the gravitational force does no work on the planet..
    d.   all of the above are correct.
    e.   none of the above is correct.

33. The period of oscillation of an object in a frictionless tunnel running through the Earth is 84.3 min. What is the period of oscillation of an object in a similar tunnel on the Moon? ($R_E = 6.37 \times 10^6$ m; $R_M = 1.74 \times 10^6$ m; $M_E = 5.98 \times 10^{24}$ kg; $M_M = 7.36 \times 10^{22}$ kg.)

    a. 6.03×10^{-3} min.
    b.   0.713 min.
    c.   84.3 min.
    d.   108.5 min.
    e.   139.6 min.

Open-Ended Problems

34. Isaac Newton was able to estimate a value for G, the universal gravitational constant, from the following data: the radius of the Earth is about 6400 km, the average density of rocks is about 5.5 g/cm^3, and $g = 9.8$ m/s^2 near the surface of the Earth. What value did Newton obtain for G?

35. At the moment of a total eclipse, the moon lies along a line from the Earth to the sun. If your normal weight is 600 N, how much is your weight decreased by the combined pull of the sun and moon?

$$M_{SUN} = 2.0 \times 10^{30} \text{ kg}, \quad r_{S\text{-}E} = 1.5 \times 10^8 \text{ km}$$

$$M_{MOON} = 7.4 \times 10^{22} \text{ kg}, r_{M\text{-}E} = 3.8 \times 10^5 \text{ km}$$

36. When a falling meteor is at a distance above the Earth's surface of 3 times the Earth's radius, what is its acceleration due to the Earth's gravity?

37. The planet Venus requires 225 days to orbit the sun, which has a mass $M = 1.99 \times 10^{30}$ kg, in an almost circular trajectory. Calculate the radius of the orbit and the orbital speed of Venus as it circles the sun.

38.   Imagine a hole is drilled down to the center of the Earth. A small mass m is dropped into the hole. Ignoring the Earth's rotation, and all sources of friction, find the speed of the mass just as it reaches the Earth's center. ($M_E = 6.0 \times 10^{24}$ kg; $R_E = 6.4 \times 10^6$ m.)

39.   Calculate the Earth's angular momentum in the approximation that treats the Earth's orbit around the sun as a circle. ($M_{Sun} = 1.99 \times 10^{30}$ kg; $T = 3.156 \times 10^7$ s; $M_E = 5.98 \times 10^{24}$ kg.)

Chapter 13

Universal Gravitation

1. b
2. d
3. b
4. d
5. b
6. a
7. b
8. d
9. d
10. c
11. b
12. c
13. a
14. a
15. a
16. d
17. a
18. c
19. b
20. b

21. a
22. d
23. d
24. c
25. b
26. b
27. b
28. c
29. e
30. c
31. b
32. e
33. d
34. $6.65 \times 10^{-11} \, \text{N} \cdot \text{m}^2/\text{kg}^2$
35. $0.37 \, \text{N}$
36. $0.613 \, \text{m/s}^2$
37. $1.08 \times 10^{11} \, \text{m}, 34.9 \, \text{km/s}$
38. $8.0 \times 10^3 \, \text{m/s}$
39. $2.68 \times 10^{40} \, \text{kg} \cdot \text{m}^2/\text{s}$

Chapter 14

Fluid Mechanics

Multiple Choice

1. A stonecutter's chisel has an edge area of 0.7 cm^2. If the chisel is struck with a force of 42 N, what is the pressure exerted on the stone?

    a. 600 N/m^2
    b. 30 000 N/m^2
    c. 300 000 N/m^2
    d. 600 000 N/m^2
    e. 6 000 N/m^2

2. When water freezes, it expands about 9 percent. What would be the pressure increase inside your automobile engine block if the water in there froze? The bulk modulus of ice is 2.0×10^9 N/m^2, and 1 ATM = 10^5 N/m^2.

    a. 18 ATM
    b. 360 ATM
    c. 1080 ATM
    d. 1800 ATM
    e. 600 ATM

3. All people come very close to being able to float in water. What therefore is the volume (in cubic meters) of a 50-kg woman?

    a. 0.007
    b. 0.035
    c. 0.050
    d. 0.070
    e. 0.085

4. Find the average density of a white dwarf star if it has a mass equal to that of the sun (2.0×10^{30} kg) and a radius equal to that of the Earth (6.4×10^6 m).

    a. 9.0×10^6 kg/m^3
    b. 1.8×10^7 kg/m^3
    c. 1.8×10^9 kg/m^3
    d. 3.6×10^{10} kg/m^3
    e. 9.0×10^7 kg/m^3

5.   Find the average density of a red giant star with a mass of 20×10^{30} kg
      (approximately 10 solar masses) and a radius of 150×10^9 m (equal to the Earth's
      distance from the sun).

      a. 1.41×10^{-4} kg/m^3
      b.   0.007 kg/m^3
      c.   1.41 kg/m^3
      d.   710 kg/m^3
      e. 1.41×10^{-3} kg/m^3

6.   Find the pressure in atmospheres at the base of Dworshak Dam if the water in
      the reservoir is 200 meters deep. (10^5 N/m^2 = 1 ATM.)

      a.   20.6 ATM
      b.   24.7 ATM
      c.   29.4 ATM
      d.   196 ATM
      e.   75 ATM

7.   Some species of whales can dive to depths of 1 kilometer. What is the total
      pressure they experience at this depth? (ρ_{sea} = 1020 kg/m^3 and
      10^5 N/m^2 = 1 ATM.)

      a.   9 ATM
      b.   90 ATM
      c.   101 ATM
      d.   111 ATM
      e.   130 ATM

8.   What is the total mass of the Earth's atmosphere? The radius of the Earth is
      6.4×10^6 m, and 1 ATM = 10^5 N/m^2.

      a. 5×10^{16} kg
      b. 1×10^{18} kg
      c. 5×10^{18} kg
      d. 1×10^{20} kg
      e. 5×10^9 kg

9.   A blimp is filled with 200 m^3 of helium. How much mass can the balloon lift? The
      density of helium is 1/7 that of air, and the density of air is 1/800 that of water.

      a.   115 kg
      b.   214 kg
      c.   315 kg
      d.   415 kg
      e.   37 kg

10.   What fraction of an iceberg is submerged? ($\rho_{ice} = 917 \text{ kg/m}^3$,
       $\rho_{sea} = 1.03 \times 10^3 \text{ kg/m}^3$.)

       a.   95%
       b.   93%
       c.   91%
       d.   89%
       e.   77%

11.   A supertanker filled with oil has a total mass of 6.1×10^8 kg. If the dimensions of
       the ship are those of a rectangular box 300 meters long, 80 meters wide, and 40
       meters high, determine how far the bottom of the ship is below sea level.
       ($\rho_{sea} = 1020 \text{ kg/m}^3$.)

       a.   10 m
       b.   15 m
       c.   20 m
       d.   25 m
       e.   30 m

12.   Determine the minimum area of a flat ice floe 1.0 meter thick if it is to support a
       2000-kg car above seawater. ($\rho_{ice} = 920 \text{ kg/m}^3$, $\rho_{sea} = 1020 \text{ kg/m}^3$.)

       a.   20 m^2
       b.   40 m^2
       c.   60 m^2
       d.   80 m^2
       e.   100 m^2

13.   A hydraulic lift raises a 2000-kg automobile when a 500-N force is applied to the
       smaller piston. If the smaller piston has an area of 10 cm^2, what is the cross-
       sectional area of the larger piston?

       a.   40 cm^2
       b.   80 cm^2
       c.   196 cm^2
       d.   392 cm^2
       e.   160 cm^2

14.   A hole is punched in a full milk carton, 10 cm below the top. What is the initial
       velocity of outflow?

       a.   1.4 m/s
       b.   2.0 m/s
       c.   2.8 m/s
       d.   3.9 m/s
       e.   2.8 m/s

15.   The water level in a reservoir is maintained at a constant level. What is the exit velocity in an outlet pipe 3.0 m below the water surface?

    a.   2.4 m/s
    b.   3.0 m/s
    c.   5.4 m/s
    d.   7.7 m/s
    e.   49 m/s

16.   Water is flowing at 4.0 m/s in a circular pipe. If the diameter of the pipe decreases to 1/2 its former value, what is the velocity of the water downstream?

    a.   1.0 m/s
    b.   2.0 m/s
    c.   8.0 m/s
    d.   16 m/s
    e.   4.0 m/s

17.   Water pressurized to 3.5×10^5 Pa is flowing at 5.0 m/s in a horizontal pipe which contracts to 1/3 its former area. What are the pressure and velocity of the water after the contraction?

    a. 2.5×10^5 Pa, 15 m/s
    b. 3.0×10^5 Pa, 10 m/s
    c. 3.0×10^5 Pa, 15 m/s
    d. 4.5×10^5 Pa, 1.5 m/s
    e. 5.5×10^5 Pa, 1.5 m/s

18.   A fountain sends water to a height of 100 meters. What must be the pressurization (above atmospheric) of the water system? 1 ATM = 10^5 N/m^2.

    a.   1.0 ATM
    b.   4.2 ATM
    c.   7.2 ATM
    d.   9.8 ATM
    e.   8.2 ATM

19.   What is the total force acting inward on a spherical bathysphere of diameter 2.00 m at an ocean depth of 1000 m? (The pressure inside the bathysphere is, hopefully, 1 ATM). ρ (sea water) = 1.02×10^3 kg/m^3.

    a. 1.26×10^4 N
    b. 1.26×10^6 N
    c. 1.26×10^8 N
    d. 1.26×10^{10} N
    e. 1.26×10^2 N

20. The pressure inside a commercial airliner is maintained at 1 ATM (10^5 N/m^2). What is the outward force exerted on a 1 m × 2 m cabin door if the outside pressure (at 10 km height) is 0.3 ATM?

a. 1.4×10^2 N
b. 1.4×10^3 N
c. 1.4×10^4 N
d. 1.4×10^5 N
e. 7.0×10^3 N

21. In a wind tunnel the pressure on the top surface of a model airplane wing is 8.8×10^4 N/m and the pressure on the bottom surface is 9.0×10^4 N/m^2. If the area of the top and bottom surfaces of each wing is 2.0 m^2, what is the total lift on the model airplane?

a. 2.0×10^3 N
b. 8.0×10^3 N
c. 1.6×10^4 N
d. 3.6×10^4 N
e. 1.0×10^3 N

22. Air within the funnel of a large tornado may have a pressure of only 0.2 ATM. What is the approximate outward force on a (5 m × 10 m) wall if a tornado suddenly envelops the house? (1 ATM = 10^5 N/m^2.)

a. 4×10^3 N
b. 4×10^4 N
c. 4×10^5 N
d. 4×10^6 N
e. 7×10^5 N

23. A Boeing 737 airliner has a mass of 20,000 kg and the total area of both wings (top or bottom) is 100 m^2. What is the pressure difference between the top and bottom surface of each wing when the airplane is in flight at a constant altitude?

a. 1960 N/m^2
b. 3920 N/m^2
c. 7840 N/m^2
d. 4560 N/m^2
e. 3070 N/m^2

24.   The siphon shown is used to transfer liquid from a higher level to a lower level. If the fluid is drawn up and is continuous through the tube, determine the velocity of flow of gasoline if the vertical distance from the liquid surface to the outlet is 1.0 m.

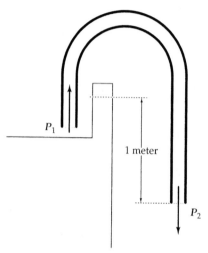

    a.   1.1 m/s
    b.   2.2 m/s
    c.   4.4 m/s
    d.   9.8 m/s
    e.   6.5 m/s

25.   A venturi tube may be used as the inlet to an automobile carburetor. If the 2.0-cm diameter pipe narrows to a 1.0-cm diameter, what is the pressure drop in the constricted section for an airflow of 3.0 cm/s in the 2.0-cm section? ($\rho = 1.2$ kg/m^3.)

    a.   70 Pa
    b.   85 Pa
    c.   100 Pa
    d.   115 Pa
    e.   81 Pa

26.   A wind of velocity 10 m/s is blowing through a wind generator with blade radius 5.0 meters. What is the maximum power output if 30% of the wind's energy can be extracted? $\rho_{air} = 1.25$ kg/m^3.

    a.   7.2 kW
    b.   14.7 kW
    c.   21.3 kW
    d.   29.4 kW
    e.   39.6 kW

27.   How much power is theoretically available from a mass flow of 1000 kg/s of water when it falls a vertical distance of 100 meters?

    a.   980 kW
    b.   98 kW
    c.   4900 W
    d.   980 W
    e.   9600 W

28.   Water is sent from a firehose at 30.0 m/s at an angle of 30° above the horizontal. What is the maximum height reached by the water?

    a.   7.50 m
    b.   11.5 m
    c.   15.0 m
    d.   19.0 m
    e.   30.0 m

29.   A thin rectangular piece of wood floats in water. You slowly pour oil with a density equal to that of the wood on the surface of the water until the height of the oil above the water is twice the height of the piece of wood. Which statement is correct?

    a.   The wood floats on top of the oil, so it sticks up in the air.
    b.   The wood does not change its position
    c.   The wood sinks below the surface of the water.
    d.   The wood is half in the water and half in the oil.
    e.   The wood floats in the oil just above the water.

30.   Two identical fish, both at sea level, float in two identical aquariums with identical quantities of water. Fish A is in Alaska, so it weighs more than fish B at the equator, since g is larger at sea level in Alaska. Which statement is correct.

    a.   A comparison is impossible unless they are both floating at the same level.
    b.   Fish A displaces a greater quantity of water than fish B.
    c.   Fish B displaces a greater quantity of water than fish A.
    d.   They both displace the same quantity of water.
    e.   Fish A has a smaller acceleration than Fish B when equal horizontal forces are applied to each, because Fish A weighs more.

31.   A waiter in a restaurant fills a pitcher full of water and ice so that water would spill out if any more were added. As the ice starts to melt

    a.   the water level in the pitcher falls.
    b.   the water level in the pitcher remains the same.
    c.   water starts to flow out the spout of the pitcher.
    d.   the pressure on the bottom of the pitcher decreases.
    e.   the pressure on the bottom of the pitcher increases.

32.   People can snorkel down to a depth of roughly one meter. This means that the maximum pressure their lungs can exert on the air they expel is roughly

    a.   9800 N.
    b.   9800 Pa.
    c.   9800 ATM.
    d.   19 600 N.
    e.   19 600 N/m^2.

33.   A wood block is placed on top of the ice in a large bowl half full of ice. The bowl is then filled to the brim with water, with the wood block riding on top of the ice. As the ice melts,

    a,   the density of the water decreases.
    b.   the water level falls below the rim.
    c.   the water level rises and water spills out of the bowl.
    d.   the water level does not change.
    e.   the wood block descends, causing water to spill out of the bowl.

34.   An empty spice bottle has an inner volume of 1.31×10^{-4} m^3. It has a mass of 112 g when filled with air, and it displaces 1.63×10^{-4} m^3 of water when fully submerged. What fraction of the total volume of the bottle will be beneath the surface when it is placed in a tank of water?

    a.   0.69
    b.   0.81
    c.   0.85
    d.   1.00
    e.   1.46

35.   An empty spice bottle has an inner volume of 1.31×10^{-4} m^3. It has a mass of 112 g when filled with air, and it displaces 1.63×10^{-4} m^3 of water when fully submerged. What volume of mercury ($\rho_{Hg} = 13.6 \times 10^3$ kg/m^3) must be added to the bottle so that it will just be submerged?

    a.   3.74 cm^3
    b.   12.0 cm^3
    c.   101 cm^3
    d.   147 cm^3
    e.   237 cm^3

36.   The figure below shows a container filled with water to the height shown. When we compare the pressure at A to the pressure at B, we find that

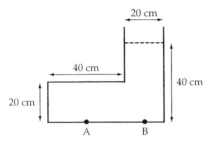

a. $p_A = \dfrac{1}{4} p_B$.

b. $p_A = \dfrac{1}{2} p_B$.

c. $p_A = p_B$.

d. $p_A = 2p_B$.

e. $p_A = 4p_B$.

37.   The water level in identical bowls, A and B, is exactly the same. A contains only water; B contains ice as well as water. When we weigh the bowls, we find that

a. $W_A < W_B$.

b. $W_A = W_B$.

c. $W_A > W_B$.

d. $W_B > W_A$ if the volume of the ice cubes is greater than $\dfrac{1}{9}$ the volume of the water.

e. $W_B > W_A$ if the volume of the ice cubes is greater than 9 times the volume of the water.

Open-Ended Problems

38.   One hundred milliliters of water is poured into a U-tube that has a cross-sectional area of 1 cm². Then 100 milliliters of oil, with a density 80% that of water, is poured down one side of the U-tube so that the oil floats on the water. Find the difference in height of the liquid surfaces on the two sides of the U-tube.

39.   A natural gas pipeline with a diameter 0.25 m delivers 1.55 cubic meters of gas per second. What is the flow speed of the gas in the pipeline?

40.   A fountain sends a stream of water 20 m up into the air. If the base of the stream is 10 cm in diameter, what power is required to send the water to this height?

Chapter 14

Fluid Mechanics

1.	d	21.	b
2.	d	22.	d
3.	c	23.	a
4.	c	24.	c
5.	e	25.	e
6.	a	26.	b
7.	c	27.	a
8.	c	28.	b
9.	b	29.	e
10.	d	30.	d
11.	d	31.	b
12.	a	32.	b
13.	d	33.	d
14.	a	34.	a
15.	d	35.	a
16.	d	36.	c
17.	a	37.	b
18.	d	38.	20 cm
19.	c	39.	31.6 m/s
20.	d	40.	30.5 kW

Chapter 15

Oscillatory Motion

Conceptual Problems

1. A body of mass 5.0 kg is suspended by a spring which stretches 10 cm when the mass is attached. It is then displaced downward an additional 5.0 cm and released. Its position as a function of time is approximately

    a. $y = .10 \sin 9.9t$
    b. $y = .10 \cos 9.9t$
    c. $y = .10 \cos (9.9t + .1)$
    d. $y = .10 \sin (9.9t + 5)$
    e. $y = .05 \cos 9.9t$

2. A body oscillates with simple harmonic motion along the x-axis. Its displacement varies with time according to the equation $x = 5.0 \sin (\pi t)$. The acceleration (in m/s^2) of the body at $t = 1.0$ s is approximately

    a. 3.5
    b. 49
    c. 14
    d. 43
    e. 4.3

3. A body oscillates with simple harmonic motion along the x axis. Its displacement varies with time according to the equation $x = 5 \sin (\pi t + \pi/3)$. The phase (in rad) of the motion at $t = 2$ s is

    a. $7\pi/3$
    b. $\pi/3$
    c. π
    d. $5\pi/3$
    e. 2π

4. A body oscillates with simple harmonic motion along the x axis. Its displacement varies with time according to the equation $x = 5.0 \sin (\pi t + \pi/3)$. The velocity (in m/s) of the body at $t = 1.0$ s is

    a. +8.0
    b. −8.0
    c. −14
    d. +14
    e. −5.0

5.   The motion of a particle connected to a spring is described by $x = 10 \sin (\pi t)$. At what time (in s) is the potential energy equal to the kinetic energy?

   a.   0
   b.   0.25
   c.   0.50
   d.   0.79
   e.   1.0

6.   The amplitude of a system moving with simple harmonic motion is doubled. The total energy will then be

   a.   4 times larger
   b.   3 times larger
   c.   2 times larger
   d.   the same as it was
   e.   half as much

7.   A mass $m = 2.0$ kg is attached to a spring having a force constant $k = 290$ N/m as in the figure. The mass is displaced from its equilibrium position and released. Its frequency of oscillation (in Hz) is approximately

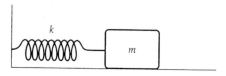

   a.   12
   b.   0.50
   c.   0.01
   d.   1.9
   e.   0.08

8.   The mass in the figure slides on a frictionless surface. If $m = 2$ kg, $k_1 = 800$ N/m and $k_2 = 500$ N/m, the frequency of oscillation (in Hz) is approximately

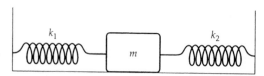

   a.   6
   b.   2
   c.   4
   d.   8
   e.   10

9.   Two circus clowns (each having a mass of 50 kg) swing on two flying trapezes (negligible mass, length 25 m) shown in the figure. At the peak of the swing, one grabs the other, and the two swing back to one platform. The time for the forward and return motion is

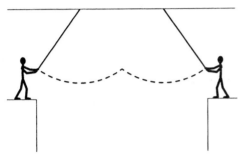

    a.   10 s
    b.   50 s
    c.   15 s
    d.   20 s
    e.   25 s

10.   A uniform rod (mass $m = 1.0$ kg and length $L = 2.0$ m) pivoted at one end oscillates in a vertical plane as shown below. The period of oscillation (in s) is approximately

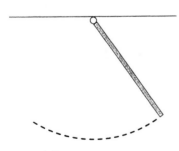

    a.   4.0
    b.   1.6
    c.   3.2
    d.   2.3
    e.   2.0

11.   A horizontal plank (m = 2.0 kg, L = 1.0 m) is pivoted at one end. A spring
      ($k = 1.0 \times 10^3$ N/m) is attached at the other end, as shown in the figure. Find the
      angular frequency (in rad/s) for small oscillations.

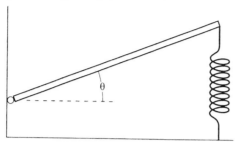

   a.   39
   b.   44
   c.   55
   d.   66
   e.   25

12.   The figure shows a uniform rod (length L = 1.0 m, mass = 2.0 kg) suspended
      from a pivot a distance d = 0.25 m above its center of mass. The angular
      frequency (in rad/s) for small oscillations is approximately

   a.   1.0
   b.   2.5
   c.   1.5
   d.   4.1
   e.   3.5

13.   In the figure below, a disk (radius R = 1.0 m, mass = 2.0 kg) is suspended from a
      pivot a distance d = 0.25 m above its center of mass. The angular frequency (in
      rad/s) for small oscillations is approximately

   a.   4.2
   b.   2.1
   c.   1.5
   d.   1.0
   e.   3.8

14.   In the figure below, a hoop (radius $R = 1.0$ m, mass $= 2.0$ kg) having four spokes of negligible mass is suspended from a pivot a distance $d = .25$ m above its center of mass. The angular frequency (in rad/s) for small oscillations is approximately

a.   4.0
b.   2.5
c.   1.5
d.   1.0
e.   0.5

15.   A torsional pendulum consists of a solid disk (mass $= 2.0$ kg, radius $= 1.0$ m) suspended by a wire attached to a rigid support. The body oscillates about the support wire. If the torsion constant is $16 \text{ N} \cdot \text{m}$. What is the angular frequency (in rad/s)?

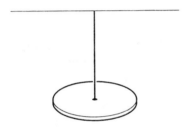

a.   2
b.   4
c.   6
d.   8
e.   7

16.   The mass in the figure below slides on a frictionless surface. When the mass is pulled out, spring 1 is stretched a distance x_1 from its equilibrium position and spring 2 is stretched a distance x_2. The spring constants are k_1 and k_2 respectively. The force pulling back on the mass is:

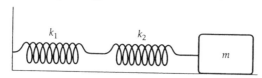

   a. $-k_2 x_1$.

   b. $-k_2 x_2$.

   c. $-(k_1 x_1 + k_2 x_2)$.

   d. $-\dfrac{k_1 + k_2}{2}(x_1 + x_2)$.

   e. $-\dfrac{k_1 + k_2}{k_1 k_2}(x_1 + x_2)$.

17.   A hoop, a solid cylinder, and a solid sphere all have the same mass m and the same radius R. Each is mounted to oscillate about an axis a distance $0.5\,R$ from the center. The axis is perpendicular to the circular plane of the hoop and the cylinder and to an equatorial plane of the sphere as shown below. Which is the correct ranking in order of increasing angular frequency ω?

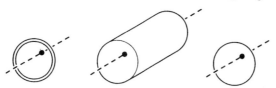

   a.   hoop, cylinder, sphere
   b.   cylinder, sphere, hoop
   c.   sphere, cylinder, hoop
   d.   hoop, sphere, cylinder
   e.   sphere, hoop, cylinder

18.   Three pendulums with strings of the same length and bobs of the same mass are pulled out to angles θ_1, θ_2 and θ_3 respectively and released. The approximation $\sin\theta = \theta$ holds for all three angles, with $\theta_3 > \theta_2 > \theta_1$. How do the angular frequencies of the three pendulums compare?

   a. $\omega_3 > \omega_2 > \omega_1$

   b.   Need to know amplitudes to answer this question.

   c.   Need to know $\sqrt{g/L}$ to answer this question.

   d. $\omega_1 > \omega_2 > \omega_3$

   e. $\omega_1 = \omega_2 = \omega_3$

19.   A weight of mass *m* is at rest at O when suspended from a spring, as shown. When it is pulled down and released, it oscillates between positions A and B. Which statement about the system consisting of the spring and the mass is correct?

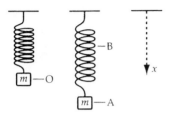

    a.   The gravitational potential energy of the system is greatest at A.
    b.   The elastic potential energy of the system is greatest at O.
    c.   The rate of change of momentum has its greatest magnitude at A and B.
    d.   The rate of change of gravitational potential energy is smallest at O.
    e.   The rate of change of gravitational potential energy has its greatest magnitude at A and B.

20.   An object of mass *m* is attached to string of length *L*. When it is released from point A, the object oscillates between points A and B. Which statement about the system consisting of the pendulum and the Earth is correct?

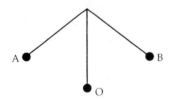

    a.   The gravitational potential energy of the system is greatest at A and B.
    b.   The kinetic energy of mass *m* is greatest at point O.
    c.   The greatest rate of change of momentum occurs at A and B.
    d.   All of the above are correct.
    e.   Only (a) and (b) above are correct.

21.   A graph of position versus time for an object oscillating at the free end of a horizontal spring is shown below. A point or points at which the object has positive velocity and zero acceleration is(are)

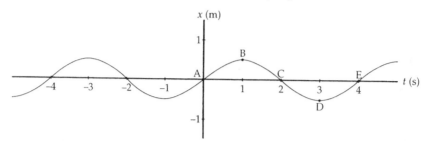

a.   B
b.   C
c.   D
d.   B or D
e.   A or E

22.   A graph of position versus time for an object oscillating at the free end of a horizontal spring is shown below. The point at which the object has negative velocity and zero acceleration is

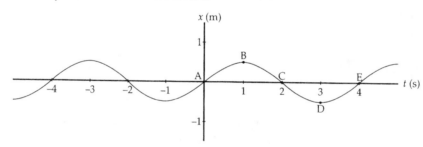

a.   A
b.   B
c.   C
d.   D
e.   E

23.   A graph of position versus time for an object oscillating at the free end of a
horizontal spring is shown below. The point at which the object has zero velocity
and positive acceleration is

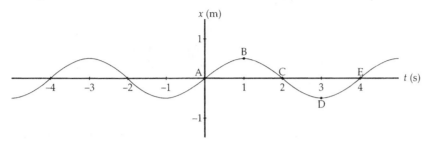

a.   A
b.   B
c.   C
d.   D
e.   E

24.   A graph of position versus time for an object oscillating at the free end of a
horizontal spring is shown below. The point at which the object has zero velocity
and negative acceleration is

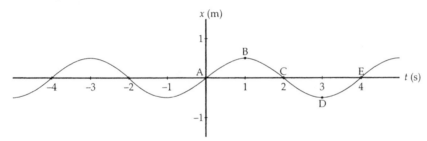

a.   A
b.   B
c.   C
d.   D
e.   E

Open-Ended Problems

25.   An automobile ($m = 1.00 \times 10^3$ kg) is driven into a brick wall in a safety test. The
bumper behaves like a spring ($k = 5.00 \times 10^6$ N/m), and is observed to compress a
distance of 3.16 cm as the car is brought to rest. What was the initial speed of the
automobile?

26.   The mat of a trampoline is held by 32 springs, each having a spring constant of
5000 N/m. A person with a mass of 40.0 kg jumps from a platform 1.93 m high
onto the trampoline. Determine the stretch of each of the springs.

27.   An archer pulls her bow string back 0.4 m by exerting a force that increases uniformly from zero to 240 N. What is the equivalent spring constant of the bow, and how much work is done in pulling the bow?

28.   An ore car of mass 4000 kg starts from rest and rolls downhill on tracks from a mine. A spring with $k = 400\,000$ N/m is located at the end of the tracks. At the spring's maximum compression, the car is at an elevation 10 m lower than its elevation at the starting point. How much is the spring compressed in stopping the ore car? Ignore friction.

29.   The motion of a piston in an auto engine is simple harmonic. If the piston travels back and forth over a distance of 10 cm, and the piston has a mass of 1.5 kg, what is the maximum speed of the piston and the maximum force acting on the piston when the engine is running at 4200 rpm?

Chapter 15

Oscillatory Motion

1.	e	16.	b
2.	d	17.	a
3.	a	18.	e
4.	b	19.	c
5.	b	20.	d
6.	a	21.	e
7.	d	22.	c
8.	c	23.	d
9.	a	24.	b
10.	d	25.	2.23 m/s (5 mph)
11.	a	26.	9.97 cm
12.	d	27.	600 N/m, 48 J
13.	b	28.	1.4 m
14.	c	29.	22 m/s, 14 500 N
15.	b		

Chapter 16

Wave Motion

Multiple Choice

1. The wavelength of light visible to the human eye is on the order of 5×10^{-7} m. If the speed of light in air is 3×10^8 m/s, find the frequency of the lightwave.

    a. 3×10^7 Hz
    b. 4×10^9 Hz
    c. 5×10^{11} Hz
    d. 6×10^{14} Hz
    e. 4×10^{15} Hz

2. The speed of a 10-kHz sound wave in seawater is approximately 1500 m/s. What is its wavelength in sea water?

    a. 5.0 cm
    b. 10 cm
    c. 15 cm
    d. 20 cm
    e. 29 cm

3. Bats can detect small objects such as insects that are of a size on the order of a wavelength. If bats emit a chirp at a frequency of 60 kHz and the speed of soundwaves in air is 330 m/s, what is the smallest size insect they can detect?

    a. 1.5 mm
    b. 3.5 mm
    c. 5.5 mm
    d. 7.5 mm
    e. 9.8 mm

4. Ocean waves with a wavelength of 120 m are coming in at a rate of 8 per minute. What is their speed?

    a. 8.0 m/s
    b. 16 m/s
    c. 24 m/s
    d. 30 m/s
    e. 4.0 m/s

5.   An earthquake emits both S-waves and P-waves which travel at different speeds through the Earth. A P-wave travels at 9000 m/s and an S-wave travels at 5000 m/s. If P-waves are received at a seismic station 1.00 minute before an S-wave arrives, how far away is the earthquake center?

    a.   88.9 km
    b.   1200 km
    c.   675 km
    d.   240 km
    e.   480 km

6.   A piano string of density 0.0050 kg/m is under a tension of 1350 N. Find the velocity with which a wave travels on the string.

    a.   260 m/s
    b.   520 m/s
    c.   1040 m/s
    d.   2080 m/s
    e.   4160 m/s

7.   A 100-m long transmission cable is suspended between two towers. If the mass density is 2.01 kg/m and the tension in the cable is 3.00×10^4 N, what is the speed of transverse waves on the cable?

    a.   60 m/s
    b.   122 m/s
    c.   244 m/s
    d.   310 m/s
    e.   1500 m/s

8.   Transverse waves are traveling on a 1.00-m long piano string at 500 m/s. If the points of zero vibration occur at one-half wavelength, (where the string is fastened at both ends), find the frequency of vibration.

    a.   250 Hz
    b.   500 Hz
    c.   1000 Hz
    d.   2000 Hz
    e.   2500 Hz

9.   The lowest A on a piano has a frequency of 27.5 Hz. If the tension in the 2.00-m string is 308 N, and one-half wavelength occupies the string, what is the mass of the wire?

    a.   0.025 kg
    b.   0.049 kg
    c.   0.051 kg
    d.   0.081 kg
    e.   0.037 kg

10. If $y = 0.02 \sin (30x - 400t)$ (SI units), the frequency of the wave is

   a. 30 Hz
   b. $15/\pi$ Hz
   c. $200/\pi$ Hz
   d. 400 Hz
   e. 800π Hz

11. If $y = 0.02 \sin (30x - 400t)$ (SI units), the wavelength of the wave is

   a. $\pi/15$ m
   b. $15/\pi$ m
   c. 60π m
   d. 4.2 m
   e. 30 m

12. If $y = 0.02 \sin (30x - 400t)$ (SI units), the velocity of the wave is

   a. 3/40 m/s
   b. 40/3 m/s
   c. $60\pi/400$ m/s
   d. $400/60\pi$ m/s
   e. 400 m/s

13. If $y = 0.02 \sin (30x - 400t)$ (SI units), the angular frequency of the wave is

   a. 30 rad/s
   b. $30/2\pi$ rad/s
   c. $400/2\pi$ rad/s
   d. 400 rad/s
   e. 40/3 rad/s

14. If $y = 0.02 \sin (30x - 400t)$ (SI units), the wave number is

   a. 30 m^{-1}
   b. $30/2\pi$ m^{-1}
   c. $400/2\pi$ m^{-1}
   d. 400 m^{-1}
   e. 60π m^{-1}

15. If $y = 0.02 \sin (30x - 400t)$ (SI units) and if the mass density of the string on which the wave propagates is .005 kg/m, then the transmitted power is

   a. 1.03 W
   b. 2.13 W
   c. 4.84 W
   d. 5.54 W
   e. 106 W

16.   Write the equation of a wave, traveling along the +x axis with an amplitude of
        0.02 m, a frequency of 440 Hz, and a speed of 330 m/sec.

   a. $y = 0.02 \sin [880\pi (x/330 - t)]$
   b. $y = 0.02 \cos [880\pi x/330 - 440t]$
   c. $y = 0.02 \sin [880\pi(x/330 + t)]$
   d. $y = 0.02 \sin [2\pi(x/330 + 440t)]$
   e. $y = 0.02 \cos [2\pi(x/330 + 440t)]$

17.   For the wave described by $y = 0.15 \sin \left[\dfrac{\pi}{16}(2x - 64t) \right]$ (SI units), determine the
        first positive x-coordinate where y is a maximum when t = 0.

   a.   16 m
   b.   8 m
   c.   4 m
   d.   2 m
   e.   13 m

18.   For the wave described by $y = 0.15 \sin \left[\dfrac{\pi}{16}(2x - 64t) \right]$ (SI units), determine
        x coordinate of the second maximum when t = 0.

   a.   20 m
   b.   18 m
   c.   24 m
   d.   28 m
   e.   16 m

19.   For the wave described by $y = 0.02 \sin (kx)$ at t = 0 s, the first maximum at a
        positive x coordinate occurs where x = 4 m. Where on the positive x axis does the
        second maximum occur?

   a.   20 m
   b.   18 m
   c.   24 m
   d.   28 m
   e.   16 m

20.   For the transverse wave described by $y = 0.15 \sin \left[\dfrac{\pi}{16}(2x - 64t) \right]$ (SI units),
        determine the maximum transverse speed of the particles of the medium.

   a.   0.192 m/s
   b. 0.6π m/s
   c.   9.6 m/s
   d.   4 m/s
   e.   2 m/s

21. Which of the following is a solution to the wave equation, $\dfrac{\partial^2 y}{\partial x^2} = \dfrac{1}{v^2}\dfrac{\partial^2 y}{\partial t^2}$?

    a. $\dfrac{e^{-x}}{x}\sin x$

    b. $(\cos kx)(\sin t)$

    c. $e^{-x}\sin \omega t$

    d. $e^{-x}\sin (kx - \omega t)$

    e. $e^{-x}\cos t$

22. Find the period of a wave of 100-m wavelength in deep water where $v = \sqrt{g\lambda/2\pi}$.

    a.   5.0 s
    b.   8.0 s
    c.   12.5 s
    d.   15 s
    e.   0.125 s

23. A piano wire of length 1.5 m vibrates so that one-half wavelength is contained on the string. If the frequency of vibration is 65 Hz, the amplitude of vibration is 3.0 mm, and the density is 15 g/m, how much energy is transmitted per second down the wire?

    a.   21 W
    b.   11 W
    c.   5.4 W
    d.   2.2 W
    e.   1.1 W

24. A student attaches a length of nylon fishing line to a fence post. She stretches it out and shakes the end of the rope in her hand back and forth to produce waves on the line. The most efficient way for her to increase the wavelength is to

    a.   increase the tension on the hose and shake the end more times per second.
    b.   decrease the tension on the hose and shake the end more times per second.
    c.   increase the tension on the hose and shake the end fewer times per second.
    d.   decrease the tension on the hose and shake the end fewer times per second.
    e.   keep the tension and frequency the same but increase the length of the hose.

25.   The figure below shows a sine wave at one point of a string as a function of time.

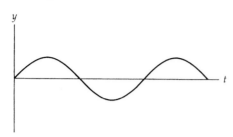

Which of the graphs below shows a wave where the amplitude and the frequency are doubled?

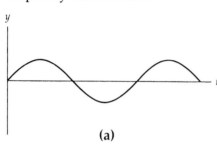

(a)

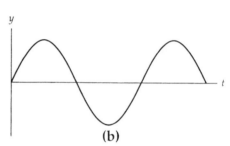

(b)

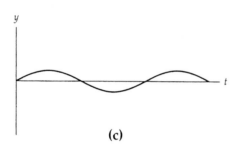

(c)

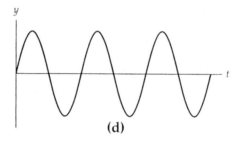

(d)

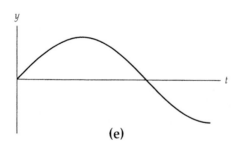

(e)

26.   The figure below shows a sine wave at one point of a string as a function of time.

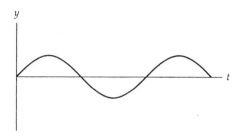

Which of the graphs below shows a wave where the amplitude and frequency are each reduced in half?

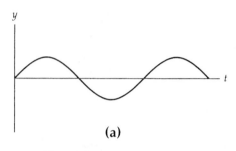

(a)

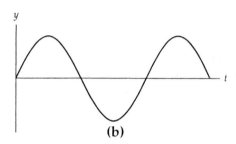

(b)

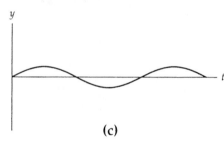

(c)

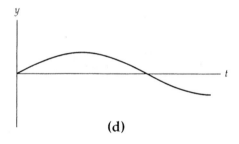

(d)

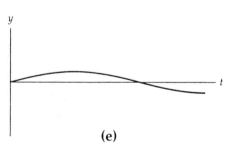

(e)

27.   The figure below shows a sine wave on a string at one instant of time.

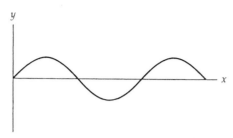

Which of the graphs below shows a wave where the frequency and wave velocity are both doubled?

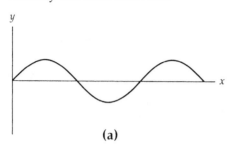

(a)

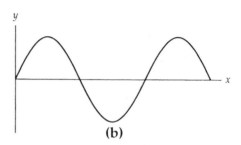

(b)

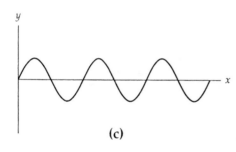

(c)

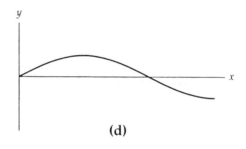

(d)

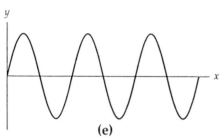

(e)

28. The figure below shows a sine wave on a string at one instant of time.

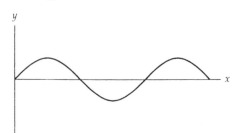

Which of the graphs below shows a wave where the wavelength is twice as large?

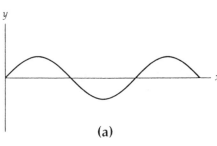

(a)

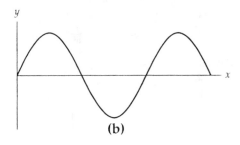

(b)

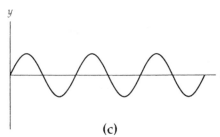

(c)

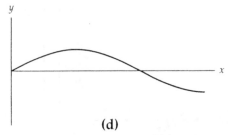

(d)

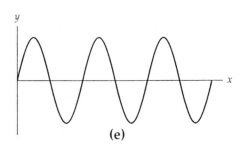

(e)

29. Superposition of waves can occur

    a. in transverse waves.
    b. in longitudinal waves.
    c. in sinusoidal waves.
    d. in all ofthe above.
    e. only in (a) and (c) above.

30.   Two pulses are traveling towards each other at 10 cm/s on a long string at $t = 0$ s, as shown below.

Which diagram below correctly shows the shape of the string at 0.5 s?

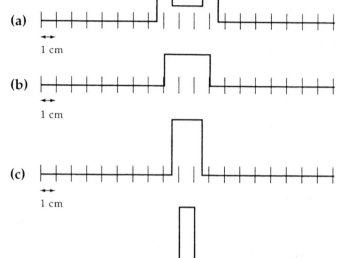

31.   Suppose that you were selected for a "Survivor"-type TV show. To help keep your group connected, you suggest that long vines can be tied together and used to transmit signals in cases of emergency. To get the signals to travel faster, you should

    a.   select lighter vines.
    b.   increase the tension on the vines.
    c.   hang weights from the vines at evenly spaced intervals.
    d.   do all of the above.
    e.   do (a) and (b) above only.

32.   Two ropes are spliced together as shown.

A short time after the incident pulse shown in the diagram reaches the splice, the ropes appearance will be that in

(a)

(b)

(c)

(d)

(e)

33.   Two ropes are spliced together as shown.

A short time after the incident pulse shown in the diagram reaches the splice, the ropes appearance will be that in

(a)

(b)

(c)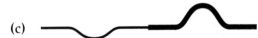

(d)

(e)

34.   The fundamental frequency of a above middle C on the piano is 440 Hz. This is the tenor high A, but a convenient note in the mid-range of women's voices. When we calculate the wavelength, we find that it is

a.   much shorter than the length of either a man's or woman's lips.
b.   shorter than the length of a man's lips, but about the length of a woman's lips.
c.   longer than a woman's lips, but about the length of a man's lips.
d.   much longer than the length of either a man's or a woman's lips.
e.   about the same length as either a man's or woman's lips.

Open-Ended Problems

35.   If the breakers at a beach are separated by 5.0 m and hit shore with a frequency of 0.20 Hz, with what speed are they traveling?

36.   Bats can detect small objects such as insects that are of a size approximately that of one wavelength. If bats emit a chirp at a frequency of 60 kHz, and the speed of sound in air is 340 m/s, what is the smallest size insect they can detect?

37.   A circus performer stretches a tightrope between two towers. He strikes one end of the rope and sends a wave along it toward the other tower. He notes that it takes 0.8 s for the wave to travel the 20 m to the opposite tower. If one meter of the rope has a mass of 0.35 kg, find the tension in the tightrope.

Chapter 16

Wave Motion

1.	d	20.	b
2.	c	21.	b
3.	c	22.	b
4.	b	23.	d
5.	c	24.	c
6.	b	25.	d
7.	b	26.	e
8.	a	27.	a
9.	c	28.	d
10.	c	29.	d
11.	a	30.	b
12.	b	31.	e
13.	d	32.	a
14.	a	33.	c
15.	b	34.	d
16.	a	35.	1.0 m/s
17.	c	36.	5.7 mm
18.	a	37.	219 N
19	a		

Chapter 17

Sound Waves

Multiple Choice

1. The velocity of sound in sea water is 1533 m/s. Find the bulk modulus (in N/m^2) of sea water if its density is $1.025 \times 10^3 \, kg/m^3$.

   a. 2.6×10^9
   b. 2.2×10^9
   c. 2.0×10^9
   d. 2.4×10^9
   e. 2.8×10^9

2. A sculptor strikes a piece of marble with a hammer. Find the speed of sound through the marble (in km/s). (The Young's modulus is $50 \times 10^9 \, N/m^2$ and its density is $2.7 \times 10^3 \, kg/m^3$.)

   a. 5.1
   b. 4.3
   c. 3.5
   d. 1.3
   e. 1.8

3. The Young's modulus for aluminum is $7.02 \times 10^{10} \, N/m^2$. If the speed of sound in aluminum is measured to be 5.10 km/s, find its density (in kg/m^3).

   a. 11.3×10^3
   b. 7.80×10^3
   c. 2.70×10^3
   d. 29.3×10^3
   e. 1.40×10^3

4. It is possible to hear an approaching train before you can see it by listening to the sound wave through the track. If the elastic modulus is $2.0 \times 10^{11} \, N/m^2$ and the density of steel is $7.8 \times 10^3 \, kg/m^3$, approximately how many times faster is the speed of sound in the track than in air? ($v_{air} \approx 340 \, m/s$.)

   a. 20
   b. 5
   c. 10
   d. 15
   e. 25

5.   A harmonic longitudinal wave propagating down a tube filled with a
        compressible gas has the form $s(x, t) = s_m \cos(kx - \omega t)$. Its velocity can be
        obtained from

        a. ω/k
        b. k/ω
        c. k
        d. ω
        e. ωk

6.   Calculate the pressure amplitude (in N/m^2) of a 500 Hz sound wave in helium if
        the displacement amplitude is equal to 5×10^{-8} m. ($\rho = 0.179$ kg/m^3, $v = 972$ m/s.)

        a. 3.5×10^{-2}
        b. 1.6×10^{-2}
        c. 2.7×10^{-2}
        d. 4.2×10^{-2}
        e. 2.0×10^{-2}

7.   Calculate the displacement amplitude (in m) of a 20 kHz sound wave in helium if
        it has a pressure amplitude of 8×10^{-3} N/m^2. ($\rho = 0.179$ kg/m^3, $v = 972$ m/s.)

        a. 2.9×10^{-10}
        b. 3.7×10^{-10}
        c. 7.8×10^{-9}
        d. 2.4×10^{-9}
        e. 1.9×10^{-10}

8.   The variation in the pressure of helium gas, measured from its equilibrium value,
        is given by $\Delta P = 2.9 \times 10^{-5} \cos(6.2x - 3000t)$ where x and t have units m and s,
        and ΔP is measured in N/m^2. Determine the frequency (in Hz) of the wave.

        a.   1500
        b.   477
        c.   1.01
        d.   0.32
        e.   239

9.   The variation in the pressure of helium gas, measured from its equilibrium value,
        is given by $\Delta P = 2.9 \times 10^{-5} \cos(6.2x - 3000t)$ where x and t have units m and s,
        and ΔP is measured in N/m^2. Determine the wavelength (in m) of the wave.

        a.   1500
        b.   0.32
        c.   477
        d.   1.01
        e.   0.50

10. The variation in the pressure of helium gas, measured from its equilibrium value, is given by $\Delta P = 2.9 \times 10^{-5} \cos(6.2x - 3000t)$ where x and t have units m and s. Determine the speed (in m/s) of the wave.

    a. 1515
    b. 153
    c. 484
    d. 828
    e. 101

11. Determine the intensity (in W/m^2) of a harmonic longitudinal wave with a pressure amplitude of 8×10^{-3} N/m^2 propagating down a tube filled with helium. ($\rho = 0.179$ kg/m^3, $v = 972$ m/s.)

    a. 3.7×10^{-7}
    b. 1.8×10^{-7}
    c. 9.2×10^{-8}
    d. 4.6×10^{-8}
    e. 1.5×10^{-9}

12. Calculate the intensity level in dB of a sound wave that has an intensity of 15×10^{-4} W/m^2.

    a. 20
    b. 200
    c. 92
    d. 9
    e. 10

13. A jet plane has a sound level of 150 dB. What is the intensity in W/m^2?

    a. 1
    b. 100
    c. 10
    d. 1000
    e. 10000

14. By what factor will an intensity change when the corresponding sound level increases by 3 dB?

    a. 3
    b. 0.5
    c. 2
    d. 4
    e. 0.3

15.   By what factor is the intensity of sound at a rock concert louder than that of a whisper when the two intensity levels are 120 dB and 20 dB respectively?

    a. 10^{12}
    b. 10^8
    c. 10^6
    d. 10^{10}
    e. 10^{11}

16.   A point source emits sound with a power output of 100 watts. What is the intensity (in W/m^2) at a distance of 10.0 m from the source?

    a. 7.96×10^{-2}
    b. 7.96×10^{-1}
    c. 7.96×10^0
    d. 7.96×10^1
    e. 7.96×10^{-3}

17.   A point source emits sound waves with a power output of 100 watts. What is the sound level (in dB) at a distance of 10 m?

    a.   139
    b.   119
    c.   129
    d.   109
    e.   10

18.   A car approaches a stationary police car at 36 m/s. The frequency of the siren (relative to the police car) is 500 Hz. What is the frequency (in Hz) heard by an observer in the moving car as he approaches the police car? (Assume the velocity of sound in air is 343 m/s.)

    a.   220
    b.   448
    c.   5264
    d.   552
    e.   383

19.   A car moving at 36 m/s passes a stationary police car whose siren has a frequency of 500 hz. What is the change in the frequency (in Hz) heard by an observer in the moving car as he passes the police car? (The speed of sound in air is 343 m/s.)

    a.   416
    b.   208
    c.   105
    d.   52
    e.   552

20.   A truck moving at 36 m/s passes a police car moving at 45 m/s in the opposite direction. If the frequency of the siren relative to the police car is 500 Hz, what is the frequency heard by an observer in the truck as the police car approaches the truck? (The speed of sound in air is 343 m/s.)

   a.   396
   b.   636
   c.   361
   d.   393
   e.   617

21.   A truck moving at 36 m/s passes a police car moving at 45 m/s in the opposite direction. If the frequency of the siren is 500 Hz relative to the police car, what is the frequency heard by an observer in the truck after the police car passes the truck? (The speed of sound in air is 343 m/s.)

   a.   361
   b.   636
   c.   393
   d.   396
   e.   383

22.   A truck moving at 36 m/s passes a police car moving at 45 m/s in the opposite direction. If the frequency of the siren is 500 Hz relative to the police car, what is the change in frequency (in Hz) heard by an observer in the truck as the two vehicles pass each other? (The speed of sound in air is 343 m/s.)

   a.   242
   b.   238
   c.   240
   d.   236
   e.   234

23.   How fast (in m/s) is the Concorde moving if it reaches Mach 1.5? (The speed of sound in air is 344 m/s.)

   a.   229
   b.   516
   c.   416
   d.   728
   e.   858

24.   A stone is thrown into a quiet pool of water. With no fluid friction, the amplitude of the waves falls off with distance r from the impact point as

   a. $1/r^3$
   b. $1/r^2$
   c. $1/r^{3/2}$
   d. $1/r^{1/2}$
   e. $1/r$

25.   A wave generated in a medium is a longitudinal wave when

    a.   there is a net transport of matter by the wave.
    b.   the molecules of the medium are unable to exert forces on each other.
    c.   molecular displacements are parallel to the wave velocity.
    d.   molecular displacements are perpendicular to the wave velocity.
    e.   the density of the medium is less than the density of water.

26.   When you hear the horn of a car that is approaching you, the frequency that you hear is larger than that heard by a person in the car because

    a.   wavecrests are farther apart by the distance the car travels in one period.
    b.   wavecrests are closer together by the distance the car travels in one period.
    c.   the car gets ahead of each wavecrest before it emits the next one.
    d.   the speed of sound in air is increased by the speed of the car.
    e.   a speeding car emits more wavecrests in each period.

27.   While you are sounding a tone on a toy whistle, you notice a friend running toward you. If you want her to hear the same frequency that you hear even though she is approaching, you must

    a.   stay put.
    b.   run towards her at the same speed.
    c.   run away from her at the same speed.
    d.   stay put and play a note of higher frequency.
    e.   run towards her and play a note of higher frequency.

28.   To decrease the intensity of the sound you are hearing from your speaker system by a factor of 36, you can

    a.   reduce the amplitude by a factor of 12 and increase your distance from the speaker by a factor of 3.
    b.   reduce the amplitude by a factor of 4 and increase your distance from the speaker by a factor of 3.
    c.   reduce the amplitude by a factor of 2 and increase your distance from the speaker by a factor of 3.
    d.   reduce the amplitude by a factor of 3 and increase your distance from the speaker by a factor of 4.
    e.   reduce the amplitude by a factor of 3 and increase your distance from the speaker by a factor of 12.

29.   Drummers like to have high-pitched cymbals that vibrate at high frequencies. To obtain the highest frequencies, a cymbal of a fixed size should be made of a material

    a.   with a low Young's modulus and a low density.
    b.   with a low Young's modulus and a high density.
    c.   with a high Young's modulus and a low density.
    d.   with a high Young's modulus and a high density.
    e.   composed of a metal-plastic laminate.

30. A person standing in the street is unaware of an bird dropping that is falling from a point directly above him with increasing velocity. If the dropping were producing sound of a fixed frequency, as it approaches the person would hear the sound

   a.   drop in frequency.
   b.   stay at the same frequency.
   c.   increase in frequency.
   d.   decrease in loudness.
   e.   stay at the same loudness.

31. (Do not try the following: it could kill you. This question is only about a hypothetical possibility.) If you were standing below an object falling at terminal velocity, as it approached you, you would hear the sound

   a.   drop in frequency.
   b.   stay at the same frequency.
   c.   increase in frequency.
   d.   decrease in loudness.
   e.   stay at the same loudness.

32. A plane wave propagating along the x-axis has the form

$$y(x,t) = (0.002\,\text{cm})\sin\left(\frac{8\pi}{\text{m}}x - \frac{2720\pi}{\text{s}}t\right).$$

   The wavelength is

   a.   0.0398 m.
   b.   0.125 m.
   c.   0.250 m.
   d.   4.00 m.
   e.   8.00 m.

33. A plane wave propagating along the x-axis has the form

$$y(x,t) = (0.002\,\text{cm})\sin\left(\frac{8\pi}{\text{m}}x - \frac{2720\pi}{\text{s}}t\right).$$

   The frequency of the wave (in Hz) is

   a. 3.68×10^{-4}.
   b. 7.35×10^{-4}.
   c.   1360.
   d.   2720.
   e. 2720π.

34. A spherical wave has the form $\psi(r,t) = \left(\dfrac{0.002\text{ cm}}{r}\right)\sin\left(\dfrac{8\pi}{\text{m}}x - \dfrac{2720\pi}{\text{s}}t\right)$. The amplitude of the wave a distance r from the source is

a. 0.002 cm.

b. $\dfrac{0.002\text{ cm}}{\sqrt{r}}$.

c. $\dfrac{0.002\text{ cm}}{r}$.

d. $\dfrac{(0.002\text{ cm})^2}{r}$.

e. $\dfrac{0.002\text{ cm}}{r^2}$.

35. A spherical wave has the form $\psi(r,t) = \left(\dfrac{0.002\text{ cm}}{r}\right)\sin\left(\dfrac{8\pi}{\text{m}}x - \dfrac{2720\pi}{\text{s}}t\right)$. The wavelength of the wave is

a. 0.25 m.
b. 0.50 m.
c. 4 m.
d. 8 m.
e. 4π m.

36. A spherical wave has the form $\psi(r,t) = \left(\dfrac{0.002\text{ cm}}{r}\right)\sin\left(\dfrac{8\pi}{\text{m}}x - \dfrac{2720\pi}{\text{s}}t\right)$. The frequency of the wave (in Hz) is

a. 3.68×10^{-4}.
b. 7.35×10^{-4}.
c. 1360.
d. 2720.
e. 2720π.

37. A spherical wave has the form $\psi(r,t) = \left(\dfrac{0.002\text{ cm}}{r}\right)\sin\left(\dfrac{8\pi}{\text{m}}x - \dfrac{2720\pi}{\text{s}}t\right)$. The velocity of the wave (in m/s) is

a. 0.00588.
b. 16.
c. 340.
d. 1360.
e. 2720.

Open-Ended Problems

38. A bat, flying at 5.00 m/s, emits a chirp at 40.0 kHz. If this sound pulse is reflected by a wall, what is the frequency of the echo received by the bat? ($v_{sound} = 340$ m/s.)

39. A microphone in the ocean is sensitive to the sounds emitted by porpoises. To produce a usable signal, sound waves striking the microphone must have an intensity of 1.02×10^{-11} W/m². If porpoises emit sounds with a power of 0.0499 W, how far away can a porpoise be and still be heard? Disregard absorption of sound waves by the water.

40. An airplane traveling at half the speed of sound emits sound at a frequency of 5000 Hz. At what frequency does a stationary listener hear the sound as the plane approaches, and after it passes by? Assume the airplane is not flying very high.

41. The intensity level of an orchestra is 85 dB. A single violin achieves a level of 70 dB. How does the intensity of the sound of the full orchestra compare with that of the violin?

42. When a workman strikes a steel pipeline with a hammer, he generates both longitudinal and transverse waves. The two types of reflected waves return 2.4 s apart. How far away is the reflection point? [For steel, $v_L = 6.2$ km/s, $v_T = 3.2$ km/s]

Chapter 17

Sound Waves

1.	d	22.	c
2.	b	23.	b
3.	c	24.	d
4.	d	25.	c
5.	a	26.	b
6.	c	27.	c
7.	b	28.	c
8.	b	29.	c
9.	d	30.	c
10.	c	31.	b
11.	b	32.	c
12.	c	33.	c
13.	d	34.	c
14.	c	35.	a
15.	d	36.	c
16.	a	37.	c
17.	d	38.	41.2 kHz
18.	d	39.	19.7 km
19.	c	40.	10 000 Hz, 3 333 Hz
20.	b	41.	$I_{Orchestra} = 31.6 I_{Violin}$
21.	d	42.	7.9 km

Chapter 18

Superposition and Standing Waves

Multiple Choice

1.   Two harmonic waves are described by

$$y_1 = (3 \text{ m}) \sin\left(\frac{4}{\text{m}} x - \frac{700}{\text{s}} t\right)$$

$$y_2 = (3 \text{ m}) \sin\left(\frac{4}{\text{m}} x - \frac{700}{\text{s}} t - 2\right)$$

What is the amplitude of the resultant wave?

   a.   8.0 m
   b.   4.3 m
   c.   6.0 m
   d.   3.2 m
   e.   3.0 m

2.   Two harmonic waves are described by

$$y_1 = (4 \text{ m}) \sin\left(\frac{8}{\text{m}} x - \frac{300}{\text{s}} t\right)$$

$$y_2 = (4 \text{ m}) \sin\left(\frac{8}{\text{m}} x - \frac{300}{\text{s}} t - 2\right)$$

What is the frequency of the resultant wave?

   a.   300
   b.   48
   c.   8
   d.   0.8
   e.   150

3.   Two harmonic waves are described by

$$y_1 = (5\,\text{m})\sin\left(\frac{6}{\text{m}}x - \frac{900}{\text{s}}t\right)$$

$$y_2 = (5\,\text{m})\sin\left(\frac{6}{\text{m}}x - \frac{900}{\text{s}}t - 2\right)$$

What is the wavelength of the resultant wave?

a.   3 m
b.   2 m
c.   1 m
d.   4 m
e.   6 m

4.   Two harmonic waves are described by

$$y_1 = (7\,\text{m})\sin\left(\frac{5}{\text{m}}x - \frac{100}{\text{s}}t\right)$$

$$y_2 = (7\,\text{m})\sin\left(\frac{5}{\text{m}}x - \frac{100}{\text{s}}t - 2\right)$$

What is the phase of the resultant wave when $x = t = 0$?

a.   3
b.   0
c.   2
d.   1
e.   4

5.   The path difference between two waves is 5m. If the wavelength of the waves emitted by the two sources is 4m, what is the phase difference (in degrees)?

a.   90
b.   400
c.   1.57
d.   7.85
e.   15

6. Two harmonic waves are described by

$$y_1 = (3\,\text{cm})\sin\left(\frac{8}{\text{m}}x + \frac{2}{\text{s}}t\right)$$

$$y_2 = (3\,\text{cm})\sin\left(\frac{8}{\text{m}}x - \frac{2}{\text{s}}t\right)$$

What is the magnitude of the speed (in m/s) of the two traveling waves?

a.   16
b.   4
c.   8
d.   0.25
e.   2

7. Two harmonic waves are described by

$$y_1 = (6\,\text{cm})\sin\left(\pi\left(\frac{8}{\text{m}}x + \frac{2}{\text{s}}t\right)\right)$$

$$y_2 = (6\,\text{cm})\sin\left(\pi\left(\frac{8}{\text{m}}x - \frac{2}{\text{s}}t\right)\right)$$

From the choices given, determine the smallest positive value of x (in cm) corresponding to a node of the resultant standing wave.

a.   3
b.   0.25
c.   0
d.   6
e.   1.5

8. Two harmonic waves are described by

$$y_1 = (6.00\,\text{cm})\sin\left(\pi\left(\frac{2.00}{\text{m}}x + \frac{3.00}{\text{s}}t\right)\right)$$

$$y_2 = (6.00\,\text{cm})\sin\left(\pi\left(\frac{2.00}{\text{m}}x - \frac{3.00}{\text{s}}t\right)\right)$$

What is the magnitude of the displacement (in cm) of this wave at $x = 3$ cm and $t = 5$ sec?

a.   12.0
b.   3.00
c.   6.00
d.   2.25
e.   0

9.   Two harmonic waves traveling in opposite directions interfere to produce a standing wave described by $y = 3 \sin (2x) \cos 5t$ where x is in m and t is in s. What is the wavelength of the interfering waves?

   a.   3.14 m
   b.   1.00 m
   c.   6.28 m
   d.   12.0 m
   e.   2.00 m

10.   Two harmonic waves traveling in opposite directions interfere to produce a standing wave described by $y = 4 \sin (5x) \cos (6t)$ where x is in m and t is in s. What is the approximate frequency of the interfering waves?

   a.   3 Hz
   b.   1 Hz
   c.   6 Hz
   d.   12 Hz
   e.   5 Hz

11.   Two harmonic waves traveling in opposite directions interfere to produce a standing wave described by $y = 2 \sin (4x) \cos (3t)$ where x is in m and t is in s. What is the speed (in m/s) of the interfering waves?

   a.   0.75
   b.   0.25
   c.   1.3
   d.   12
   e.   3.0

12.   Two harmonic waves traveling in opposite directions interfere to produce a standing wave described by $y = 2 \sin (\pi x) \cos (3\pi t)$ where x is in m and t is in s. What is the distance (in m) between the first two antinodes?

   a.   8
   b.   2
   c.   4
   d.   1
   e.   0.5

13.   A string is stretched and fixed at both ends, 200 cm apart. If the density of the string is 0.015 g/cm, and its tension is 600 N, what is the wavelength (in cm) of the first harmonic?

   a.   600
   b.   400
   c.   800
   d.   1000
   e.   200

14. A string is stretched and fixed at both ends, 200 cm apart. If the density of the string is 0.015 g/cm, and its tension is 600 N, what is the fundamental frequency?

    a.   316 Hz
    b.   632 Hz
    c.   158 Hz
    d.   215 Hz
    e.   79 Hz

15. A stretched string is observed to vibrate in three equal segments when driven by a 480 Hz oscillator. What is the fundamental frequency of vibration for this string?

    a.   480 Hz
    b.   320 Hz
    c.   160 Hz
    d.   640 Hz
    e.   240 Hz

16. A clarinet behaves like a tube closed at one end. If its length is 1.0 m, and the velocity of sound is 344 m/s, what is its fundamental frequency (in Hz)?

    a.   264
    b.   140
    c.   86
    d.   440
    e.   172

17. An organ pipe open at both ends has a radius of 4.0 cm and a length of 6.0 m. What is the frequency (in Hz) of the third harmonic? (Assume the velocity of sound is 344 m/s.)

    a.   76
    b.   86
    c.   54
    d.   28
    e.   129

18. A vertical tube one meter long is open at the top. It is filled with 75 cm of water. If the velocity of sound is 344 m/s, what will the fundamental resonant frequency be (in Hz)?

    a.   3.4
    b.   172
    c.   344
    d.   1.7
    e.   688

19.   A length of organ pipe is closed at one end. If the speed of sound is 344 m/s, what length of pipe (in cm) is needed to obtain a fundamental frequency of 50 Hz?

   a.   28
   b.   86
   c.   344
   d.   172
   e.   688

20.   Two tuning forks with frequencies 264 and 262 Hz produce "beats". What is the beat frequency (in Hz)?

   a.   4
   b.   2
   c.   1
   d.   3
   e.   0 (no beats are produced)

21.   Two instruments produce a beat frequency of 5 Hz. If one has a frequency of 264 Hz, what could be the frequency of the other instrument?

   a.   269 Hz
   b.   254 Hz
   c.   264 Hz
   d.   5 Hz
   e.   274 Hz

22.   Two waves are described by

   $y_1 = 6 \cos 180t$ and $y_2 = 6 \cos 186t$, (both in meters).

   With what angular frequency does the maximum amplitude of the resultant wave vary with time?

   a.   366 rad/s
   b.   6 rad/s
   c.   3 rad/s
   d.   92 rad/s
   e.   180 rad/s

23.   Two waves are described by

   $y_1 = 6 \cos 180t$ and $y_2 = 6 \cos 186t$, (both in meters).

   What effective frequency does the resultant vibration have at a point?

   a.   92 Hz
   b.   183 Hz
   c.   6 Hz
   d.   3 Hz
   e.   366 Hz

24.   An organ pipe open at both ends is 1.5 m long. A second organ pipe that is
closed at one end and open at the other is 0.75 m long. The speed of sound in the
room is 330 m/s. Which of the following sets of frequencies consists of
frequencies which can be produced by *both* pipes?

    a.   110 Hz, 220 Hz, 330 Hz
    b.   220 Hz, 440 Hz, 660 Hz
    c.   110 Hz, 330 Hz, 550 Hz
    d.   330 Hz, 440 Hz, 550 Hz
    e.   220 Hz, 660 Hz, 1100 Hz

25.   Two strings are respectively 1.00 m and 2.00 m long. Which of the following
wavelengths, in meters, could represent harmonics present on *both* strings?

    a.   0.800, 0.670, 0.500
    b.   1.33, 1.00, 0.500
    c.   2.00, 1.00, 0.500
    d.   2.00, 1.33, 1.00
    e.   4.00, 2.00, 1.00

26.   Two point sources emit sound waves of 1.0-m wavelength. The sources, 2.0 m
apart, as shown below, emit waves which are in phase with each other at the
instant of emission. Where, along the line between the sources, are the waves out
of phase with each other by π radians?

S_1 S_2

  0   0.5   1.0   1.5   2.0 x

    a. $x = 0$, 1.0 m, 2.0 m
    b. $x = 0.50$ m, 1.5 m
    c. $x = 0.50$ m, 1.0 m, 1.5 m
    d. $x = 0.75$ m, 1.25 m
    e. $x = 0.25$ m, 0.75 m, 1.25 m, 1.75 m

27.   Two identical strings have the same length and same mass per unit length. String
B is stretched with four times as great a tension as that applied to string A.
Which statement is correct for all n harmonics on the two strings, $n = 1, 2, 3...$?

    a. $f_{n,B} = \dfrac{1}{4} f_{n,A}$.

    b. $f_{n,B} = \dfrac{1}{2} f_{n,A}$.

    c. $f_{n,B} = \sqrt{2}\, f_{n,A}$.
    d. $f_{n,B} = 2 f_{n,A}$.
    e. $f_{n,B} = 4 f_{n,A}$.

28.   The superposition of two waves

$$y_1 = (0.006 \text{ cm})\cos\left[2\pi\left(\frac{156}{\text{s}}t\right)\right] \text{ and } y_2 = (0.004 \text{ cm})\cos\left[2\pi\left(\frac{150}{\text{s}}t\right)\right]$$

at the location $x = 0$ in space results in

a.   beats at a beat frequency of 3 Hz.
b.   a pure tone at a frequency of 153 Hz.
c.   a pure tone at a frequency of 156 Hz.
d.   beats at a beat frequency of 6 Hz in a 153 Hz tone.
e.   a tone at a frequency of 156 Hz, as well as beats at a beat frequency of 6 Hz in a 153 Hz tone.

29.   The superposition of two waves,

$$y_1 = (2 \times 10^{-8} \text{ m})\sin\left[\pi\left(\frac{x}{2\text{ m}} - \frac{170}{\text{s}}t\right)\right]$$

and

$$y_2 = (2 \times 10^{-8} \text{ m})\sin\left[\pi\left(\frac{x}{2\text{ m}} - \frac{170}{\text{s}}t - \frac{1}{2}\right)\right],$$

results in a wave with a phase angle of

a.   0 rad.
b.   0.5 rad.
c. $\dfrac{\pi}{4}$ rad.
d. $\dfrac{\pi}{2}$ rad.
e. π rad.

30.   The superposition of two waves,

$$y_1 = (2 \times 10^{-8} \text{ m})\sin\left[\pi\left(\frac{x}{2\text{ m}} - \frac{170}{\text{s}}t\right)\right]$$

and

$$y_2 = (2 \times 10^{-8} \text{ m})\sin\left[\pi\left(\frac{x}{2\text{ m}} - \frac{170}{\text{s}}t - \frac{1}{2}\right)\right],$$

results in a wave with a wavelength of

a. $\dfrac{\pi}{2}$ m.
b.   2 m.
c. π m.
d.   4 m.
e. 4π m.

31. The superposition of two waves,

$$y_1 = (2 \times 10^{-8} \text{ m}) \sin \left[\pi \left(\frac{x}{2\,\text{m}} - \frac{170}{\text{s}} t \right) \right]$$

and

$$y_2 = (2 \times 10^{-8} \text{ m}) \sin \left[\pi \left(\frac{x}{2\,\text{m}} - \frac{170}{\text{s}} t - \frac{1}{2} \right) \right],$$

results in a wave with a frequency of

a. 85 Hz.
b. 170 Hz.
c. 85π Hz.
d. 340 Hz.
e. 170π Hz.

32. In a standing wave, not necessarily at the fundamental frequency, on a string of length L, the distance between nodes is

a. $\lambda/4$.
b. $\lambda/2$.
c. λ.
d. $L/4$.
e. $L/2$.

33. Which of the following wavelengths could *NOT* be present as a harmonic on a 2 m long string?

a. 4 m
b. 2 m
c. 1 m
d. 0.89 m
e. 0.5 m

34. Which of the following wavelengths could *NOT* be present as a standing wave in a 2 m long organ pipe open at both ends?

a. 4 m
b. 2 m
c. 1 m
d. 0.89 m
e. 0.5 m

35. Which of the following frequencies could *NOT* be present as a standing wave in a 2m long organ pipe open at both ends. The fundamental frequency is 85 Hz.

a. 85 Hz.
b. 170 Hz.
c. 255 Hz.
d. 340 Hz.
e. 382 Hz.

36.   An observer stands 3 m from speaker A and 4 m from speaker B. Both speakers, oscillating in phase, produce 170 Hz waves. The speed of sound in air is 340 m/s. What is the phase difference (in radians) between the waves from A and B at the observer's location, point P?

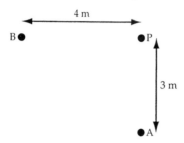

a.   0

b. $\dfrac{\pi}{2}$

c. π

d. 2π

e. 4π

Open-Ended Problems

37.   A student wants to establish a standing wave on a wire 1.8 m long clamped at both ends. The wave speed is 540 m/s. What is the minimum frequency she should apply to set up standing waves?

38.   Find the frequencies of the first three harmonics of a 1.0-m long string which has a mass per unit length of 2.0×10^{-3} kg/m and a tension of 80 N when both ends are fixed in place.

39.   A steel wire in a piano has a length of 0.70 m and a mass of 4.3 grams. To what tension must this wire be stretched to make the fundamental frequency correspond to middle C, ($f_c = 261.6$ Hz)?

Chapter 18

Superposition and Standing Waves

1.	d	21.	a
2.	b	22.	c
3.	c	23.	b
4.	d	24.	c
5.	a	25.	c
6.	d	26.	d
7.	c	27.	d
8.	d	28.	e
9.	a	29.	c
10.	b	30.	d
11.	a	31.	a
12.	d	32.	b
13.	b	33.	d
14.	c	34.	d
15.	c	35.	e
16.	c	36.	c
17.	b	37.	150 Hz
18.	c	38.	100 Hz, 200 Hz, 300 Hz
19.	d	39.	824 N
20.	b		

Chapter 19

Temperature

Multiple Choice

1. In order to understand the concept of temperature it is necessary to understand

    a.   the zeroth law of thermodynamics.
    b.   the first law of thermodynamics.
    c.   the second law of thermodynamics.
    d.   all of the above.
    e.   only (b) and (c) above.

2. In order for two objects to have the same temperature, they must

    a.   be in thermal equilibrium.
    b.   be in thermal contact with each other.
    c.   have the same relative "hotness" or "coldness" when touched.
    d.   have all of the properties listed above.
    e.   have only properties (b) and (c) above.

3. A pressure of 10 mm Hg is measured at the triple-point of water using a constant-volume gas thermometer, what will the pressure be (in mm Hg) at 50°C?

    a.   68.3
    b.   1.8
    c.   31.8
    d.   11.8
    e.   8.5

4. A pressure of 10 mm Hg is measured using a constant-volume gas thermometer at a temperature of 50°C. What is the pressure (in mm Hg) at the zero-point temperature?

    a.   31.8
    b.   11.8
    c.   8.5
    d.   54.6
    e.   68.3

5. A temperature difference of 5 K is equal to

    a.   a difference of 9 on the Celsius scale.
    b.   a difference of 9 on the Fahrenheit scale.
    c.   a difference of 2.8 on the Rankine scale.
    d.   a difference of .5 on the Fahrenheit scale.
    e.   a difference of 2.8 on the Celsius scale.

6.   A thermometer registers a change in temperature of 100°F. What change in temperature does this correspond to on the Kelvin Scale?

   a.   453
   b.   328
   c.   180
   d.   55.6
   e.   24.5

7.   Helium condenses into the liquid phase at approximately 4 K. What temperature, in degrees Fahrenheit, does this correspond to?

   a.   −182
   b.   −269
   c.   −118
   d.   −452
   e.   −484

8.   Two thermometers are calibrated, one in degrees Celsius and the other in degrees Fahrenheit. At what temperature (in kelvins) do their readings measure the same temperature?

   a.   218.15
   b.   233.15
   c.   273.15
   d.   40.15
   e.   0

9.   A child has a temperature of 104°F. What is the temperature in degrees kelvin?

   a.   40
   b.   406
   c.   401
   d.   313
   e.   349

10.   At what temperature is the Celsius scale reading equal to twice the Fahrenheit scale reading?

   a.   −12.3°F
   b.   −24.6°F
   c.   −12.3°C
   d.   −6.1°C
   e.   −20°F

11.   A bridge is made with segments of concrete 50 m long. If the linear expansion coefficient is $12 \times 10^{-6} \, (°C)^{-1}$, how much spacing (in cm) is needed to allow for expansion during an extreme temperature change of 150°F?

    a.   10
    b.   2.5
    c.   7.5
    d.   5.0
    e.   9.5

12.   A building made with a steel structure is 650 m high on a winter day when the temperature is 0°F. How much taller (in cm) is the building when it is 100°F? (The linear expansion coefficient of steel is $11 \times 10^{-6} (°C)^{-1}$.)

    a.   71
    b.   36
    c.   40
    d.   46
    e.   65

13.   A gallon container is filled with gasoline. How many gallons are lost if the temperature increases by 25°F? (The volume expansion of gasoline is $9.6 \times 10^{-4} \, (°C)^{-1}$.) (Neglect the change in volume of the container.)

    a. 2.4×10^{-2}
    b. 1.3×10^{-2}
    c. 3.6×10^{-2}
    d. 4.8×10^{-2}
    e. 9.6×10^{-2}

14.   An auditorium has dimensions 10 m × 10 m × 60 m. How many moles of air fill this volume at STP?

    a. 2.7×10^{2}
    b. 2.7×10^{4}
    c. 2.7×10^{3}
    d. 2.7×10^{5}
    e. 2.7×10^{6}

15.   An auditorium has a volume of $6 \times 10^{3} \, m^{3}$. How many molecules of air are needed to fill the auditorium at STP?

    a. 1.6×10^{29}
    b. 1.6×10^{27}
    c. 1.6×10^{25}
    d. 1.6×10^{23}
    e. 1.6×10^{20}

16.   One mole of an ideal gas is held at a constant pressure of 1 atm. Find the change in volume (in liters) if the temperature changes by 50°C.

    a.   1
    b.   2
    c.   3
    d.   4
    e.   5

17.   One mole of an ideal gas is held at a constant volume of 1 liter. Find the change in pressure if the temperature increases by 50°C.

    a.   3 atm
    b.   4 atm
    c.   2 atm
    d.   1 atm
    e.   5 atm

18.   One mole of an ideal gas has a temperature of 25°C. If the volume is held constant and the pressure is doubled, the final temperature (in °C) will be

    a.   174
    b.   596
    c.   50
    d.   323
    e.   25

19.   A bicycle pump contains air at STP. As the tire is pumped up, the volume of air decreases by 50% with each stroke. What is the new pressure of air (in atm) in the chamber after the first stroke, assuming no temperature change?

    a.   2
    b.   1
    c.   0.5
    d.   0.1
    e.   3

20.   A helium-filled balloon has a volume of 1 m³. As it rises in the earth's atmosphere, its volume expands. What will its new volume be (in m³) if its original temperature and pressure are 20°C and 1 atm, and its final temperature and pressure are –40°C and 0.1 atm?

    a.   4
    b.   6
    c.   8
    d.   10
    e.   1.5

21.   A bubble having a diameter of 1.00 cm is released from the bottom of a
        swimming pool where the depth is 5.00 m. What will the diameter of the bubble
        be when it reaches the surface? The temperature of the water at the surface is
        20.0°C, whereas it is 15.0°C at the bottom. (The density of water is
        1.00×10^3 kg/m^3.)

        a.   1.05
        b.   1.15
        c.   1.45
        d.   1.65
        e.   1.35

22.   A scuba diver has his lungs filled to half capacity (3 liters) when 10 m below the
        surface. If the diver holds his breath while quietly rising to the surface, what will
        the volume of the lungs be (in liters) at the surface? Assume the temperature is
        the same at all depths. (The density of water is 1.0×10^3 kg/m^3.)

        a.   5.9
        b.   4.5
        c.   6.4
        d.   3.9
        e.   3.1

23.   Two identical containers, A and B, hold equal amounts of the same ideal gas at
        the same P_o, V_o and T_o. The pressure of A then decreases by a half while its
        volume doubles; the pressure of B doubles while its volume decreases by a half.
        Which statement correctly describes the temperatures of the gases after the
        changes?

        a. $T_A = 0.5T_B = T_o$.
        b. $T_B = 0.5T_A = T_o$.
        c. $T_B = T_A = T_o$.
        d. $T_A = 2T_B = T_o$.
        e. $T_B = 2T_A = T_o$.

24.   Which of the following is not a possible thermometric property of a body?

        a.   The change in length of a solid.
        b.   the change in volume of a gas at constant pressure.
        c.   The change in pressure of a gas at constant volume.
        d.   The change in weight at constant pressure and volume.
        e.   The change in electrical resistance of a conductor.

25.   A pebble size object and a bowling ball size probe from a spaceship land on a large asteroid that is far from any star. After a long period of time has passed, it is highly probable that the pebble and the probe

    a.   have each had the same change in temperature.
    b.   have each had the same change in volume.
    c.   are in thermal equilibrium with one another.
    d.   are not in thermal equilibrium with one another.
    e.   are in thermal equilibrium with one another, but are not at the same temperature.

26.   A temperature difference of 9 Celsius degrees is equal to a Fahrenheit temperature difference of

    a.   5 Fahrenheit degrees.
    b.   9 Fahrenheit degrees.
    c.   16 Fahrenheit degrees.
    d.   37 Fahrenheit degrees.
    e.   41 Fahrenheit degrees.

27.   Death Valley in California receives many German tourists. When you convert a summer temperature reading of 130°F to the Celsius scale they use at home, you find that the Celsius temperature is

    a.   26°C.
    b.   54°C.
    c.   72°C.
    d.   176°C
    e.   327°C.

28.   A beaker is filled to the 500 ml mark with alcohol. What increase in volume (in ml) the beaker contain when the temperature changes from 5°C to 30°C? (Neglect the expansion of the beaker, evaporation of alcohol and absorption of water vapor by alcohol.) $\beta_{alcohol} = 1.12 \times 10^{-4} / °C$

    a.   0.47
    b.   0.93
    c.   1.4
    d.   1.7
    e.   2.5

29.   What is the change in area (in cm^2) of a 60.0 cm by 150 cm automobile windshield when the temperature changes from 0°C to 36.0°C. The coefficient of linear expansion of glass is $9 \times 10^{-6} / °C$.

    a.   1.62
    b.   2.92
    c.   3.24
    d.   4.86
    e.   5.83

30.   A container with a one-liter capacity at 27°C is filled with helium to a pressure of 2 atm. (1 atm = 1.0×10^5 N/m^2.) How many moles of helium does it hold?

    a.   0.040
    b.   0.080
    c.   0.45
    d.   0.90
    e.   1.0

Open-Ended Problems

31.   A gold ring has an inner diameter of 2.168 cm at a temperature of 15.0°C. Determine its diameter at 100°C. ($\alpha_{GOLD} = 1.42 \times 10^{-5}/°C$)

32.   Determine the change in length of a 20-m railroad track made of steel if the temperature is changed from –15°C to +35°C. ($\alpha_{STEEL} = 1.1 \times 10^{-5}/°C$)

33.   At what Fahrenheit temperature are the Kelvin and Fahrenheit temperatures numerically equal?

34.   Suppose the ends of a 30-m long steel beam are rigidly clamped at 0°C to prevent expansion. The beam has a cross-sectional area of 30 cm^2. What force against the clamps does the beam exert when it is heated to 40°C? [$\alpha_{Steel} = 1.1 \times 10^{-5}/°C$, $Y_{Steel} = 20 \times 10^{10}$ N/m^2].

35.   The pressure of a substance is directly proportional to its volume when the temperature is held constant and inversely proportional to its temperature when the volume is held constant. Is this substance an ideal gas? Explain why your answer is correct.

Chapter 19

Temperature

1.	a	21.	b
2.	a	22.	a
3.	d	23.	c
4.	c	24.	d
5.	b	25.	c
6.	d	26.	c
7.	d	27.	b
8.	b	28.	c
9.	d	29.	e
10.	a	30.	b
11.	d	31.	2.171 cm
12.	c	32.	1.1 cm
13.	b	33.	574°F = 574 K
14.	d	34.	2.6×10^5 N
15.	a		
16.	d		
17.	b		
18.	d		
19.	a		
20.	c		

35. No. Since $P = kV$ and $P = k'/T$ for fixed temperature and volume, the substance obeys the law:
$\dfrac{P_1 T_1}{V_1} = \dfrac{P_2 T_2}{V_2}$ which is different from the relation for an ideal gas.

Chapter 20

Heat and the First Law of Thermodynamics

Multiple Choice

1. Determine the heat capacity (in calories/°C) of a lake containing one million gallons (approximately 4 million kilograms) of water at 15°C.

    a. 4×10^6
    b. 4×10^9
    c. 4×10^3
    d. 1×10^3
    e. 4×10^2

2. How many calories of heat are required to raise the temperature of 4 kg of water from 50°F to the boiling point?

    a. 6.5×10^5
    b. 3.6×10^5
    c. 15×10^5
    d. 360
    e. 4×10^4

3. A 5-gallon container of water (approximately 20 kg) having a temperature of 212°F is added to a 50-gallon tub (approximately 200 kg) of water having a temperature of 50°F. What is the final equilibrium temperature (in °C) of the mixture?

    a. 54
    b. 36
    c. 18
    d. 66
    e. 14

4. A 5-kg piece of lead (specific heat 0.03 cal/g · °C) having a temperature of 80°C is added to 500 g of water having a temperature of 20°C. What is the final equilibrium temperature (in °C) of the system?

    a. 79
    b. 26
    c. 54
    d. 34
    e. 20

5.   A 300-g glass thermometer initially at 25°C is put into 200 cm³ of hot water at 95°C. Find the final temperature (in °C) of the thermometer, assuming no heat flows to the surroundings. (The specific heat of glass is 0.2 cal/g °C.)

    a.   52
    b.   68
    c.   89
    d.   79
    e.   36

6.   How much heat (in kilocalories) is needed to convert 1.00 kg of ice at 0°C into steam at 100°C?

    a.   23.9
    b.   79.6
    c.   564
    d.   643
    e.   720

7.   If 25 kg of ice at 0°C is combined with 4 kg of steam at 100°C, what will be the final equilibrium temperature (in °C) of the system?

    a.   40
    b.   20
    c.   60
    d.   100
    e.   8

8.   How much heat (in kcal) must be removed to make ice at –10°C from 2 kg of water at 20°C? (The specific heat of ice is 0.5 cal/g °C.)

    a.   190
    b.   200
    c.   240
    d.   210
    e.   50

9.   The R value of fiberglass batting, 3.5 inches thick, is 11 ft² °F h/BTU. What is the thermal conductivity (in BTU/ft · °F · s)

    a. 7.4×10^{-6}
    b. 2.7×10^{-2}
    c. 8.9×10^{-5}
    d. 1.4×10^{-4}
    e. 3.6×10^{-3}

10. A slab of concrete and an insulating board are in thermal contact with each other. The temperatures of their outer surfaces are 68°F and 50°F. Determine the rate of heat transfer (in BTU/ft² h) if the R values are 1.93 and 8.7 ft² °F h/BTU, respectively.

    a.   9.7
    b.   2.5
    c.   5.3
    d.   1.7
    e.   28

11. A wall is constructed of a 2 inch layer of fiberglass board ($R = 8$) and six inches of fiberglass batting ($R = 19$). If the temperature on the outside surface of the fiberglass board is 50°F and the temperature on the inside surface of the fiberglass batting is 68°F, what is the temperature (in °F) at the interface? (The units of R are ft² °F h/BTU.)

    a.   62
    b.   58
    c.   55
    d.   65
    e.   52

12. A cup of coffee is enclosed on all sides in an insulated cup 1/2 cm thick in the shape of a cube 10 cm on a side. The temperature of the coffee is 95°C, and the temperature of the surroundings is 21°C. Find the rate of heat loss (in J/s) due to conduction if the thermal conductivity of the cup is 2×10^{-4} cal/s · cm · °C.

    a.   62
    b.   74
    c.   230
    d.   160
    e.   12

13. A child has a temperature of 101°F. If her total cross-sectional area is 2 m², find the energy lost each second (in W) due to radiation, assuming the emissivity is 1. (Assume the room temperature is 70°F.)

    a.   217
    b.   180
    c.   90
    d.   68
    e.   850

14.   A super-insulated house is at a temperature of 20°C. The temperature outside is
       0°C. The surface area of the house is 200 m², and the emissivity is 1.
       Approximately how much energy is radiated (in W) per second.

       a.   20 000
       b.   2000
       c.   200
       d.   2
       e.   0.2

15.   A 100-kg student eats a 200-Calorie doughnut. To "burn it off", he decides to
       climb the steps of a tall building. How high (in m) would he have to climb to
       expend an equivalent amount of work? (1 food Calorie = 10^3 calories.)

       a.   273
       b.   623
       c.   418
       d.   854
       e.   8400

16.   A 5-g coin is dropped from a 300-m building. If it reaches a terminal velocity of
       45 m/s, and the rest of the energy is converted to heating the coin, what is the
       change in temperature (in °C) of the coin? (The specific heat of copper is
       387 J/kg °C.)

       a.   9
       b.   2
       c.   5
       d.   21
       e.   0.5

17.   The work done in the expansion from an initial to a final state

       a.   is the area under the curve of a PV diagram.
       b.   depends only on the end point.
       c.   is independent of the path.
       d.   is the slope of a PV curve.
       e.   equals $P(V_F - V_i)$

18.   Gas in a container expands at a constant pressure of 3 atm. Find the work done
       (in J) by the gas if the initial volume is 5 liters and the final volume is 10 liters.

       a.   0
       b.   150
       c.   15
       d.   1500
       e.   1.5

19. Gas in a container increases its pressure from 1 atm to 3 atm while keeping its volume constant. Find the work done (in J) by the gas if the volume is 5 liters.

    a.   0
    b.   3
    c.   5
    d.   15
    e. 15×10^2

20. In an adiabatic free expansion

    a.   no heat is transferred between a system and its surroundings.
    b.   the pressure remains constant.
    c.   the temperature remains constant.
    d.   the volume remains constant.
    e.   the process is reversible.

21. In an isothermal process

    a.   the volume remains constant.
    b.   the temperature remains constant.
    c.   no heat is transferred between a system and its surroundings.
    d.   the pressure remains constant.
    e.   the internal energy is not constant.

22. In an isobaric process

    a.   the volume remains constant.
    b.   the temperature remains constant.
    c.   the pressure remains constant.
    d.   no heat is transferred between a system and its surroundings.
    e.   the internal energy is constant

23. In an isovolumetric process

    a.   the temperature remains constant.
    b.   no heat is transferred between a system and its surroundings.
    c.   the pressure remains constant.
    d.   the volume remains constant.
    e.   the internal energy is constant.

24. Determine the work done by 5 moles of an ideal gas that is kept at 100°C in an expansion from 1 liter to 5 liters.

    a. 2.5×10^4 J
    b. 1.1×10^4 J
    c. 6.7×10^3 J
    d. 2.9×10^3 J
    e. 8.4×10^3 J

25.   One gram of water is heated from 0°C to 100°C at a constant pressure of 1 atm. Determine the approximate change in internal energy (in cal) of the water.

    a.   160
    b.   130
    c.   100
    d.   180
    e.   50

26.   Five moles of an ideal gas expands isothermally at 100°C to five times its initial volume. Find the heat flow into the system.

    a. 2.5×10^4 J
    b. 1.1×10^4 J
    c. 6.7×10^3 J
    d. 2.9×10^3 J
    e. 7.0×10^2 J

27.   An 8,000-kg aluminum flagpole 100-m long is heated by the sun from a temperature of 10°C to 20°C. Find the work done (in J) by the aluminum if the linear expansion coefficient is 24×10^{-6} (°C)$^{-1}$. (The density of aluminum is 2.7×10^3 kg/m^3 and 1 atm = 1.0×10^5 N/m^2.)

    a.   287
    b.   425
    c.   213
    d.   710
    e.   626

28.   An 8 000-kg aluminum flagpole 100-m long is heated by the sun from a temperature of 10°C to 20°C. Find the heat transferred (in J) to the aluminum if the specific heat of aluminum is 0.215 cal/g °C.

    a. 7.2×10^5
    b. 7.2×10^7
    c. 7.2×10^3
    d. 7.2×10^1
    e. 7.2×10^2

29.   An 8 000-kg aluminum flagpole 100-m high is heated by the sun from a temperature of 10°C to 20°C. Find the increase in internal energy (in J) of the aluminum. (The coefficient of linear expansion is 24×10^{-6} (°C)$^{-1}$, the density is 2.7×10^3 kg/m^3, and the specific heat of aluminum is 0.215 cal/g °C.)

    a. 7.2×10^5
    b. 7.2×10^7
    c. 7.2×10^3
    d. 7.2×10^1
    e. 7.2×10^2

30.   Two kilograms of water at 100°C is converted to steam at 1 atm. Find the work done (in J). (The density of steam at 100°C is 0.598 kg/m³.)

    a. 3.4×10^5
    b. 1.2×10^5
    c. 4.6×10^4
    d. 2.1×10^4
    e. 3.4×10^4

31.   Two kilograms of water at 100°C is converted to steam at 1 atm. Find the change in internal energy (in J). (L_v=2.26 × 10⁶ J/kg.)

    a. 2.1×10^4
    b. 4.5×10^6
    c. 3.4×10^5
    d. 4.2×10^6
    e. 2.1×10^6

32.   If an object feels cold to the touch, the only statement that you can make that must be correct is that

    a.   the object has a smaller coefficient of thermal conductivity than your hand.
    b.   the volume of the object will increase while it is in contact with your hand.
    c.   the object contains less thermal energy than your hand.
    d.   the object is at a lower temperature than your hand.
    e.   the object cannot be a liquid.

33.   Which of the following statements is correct?

    a.   You only need to know the amount of thermal energy a body contains to calculate its temperature.
    b.   The temperature of a body is directly proportional to the amount of work the body has performed.
    c.   The quantity of thermal energy exchanged by two bodies in contact is inversely proportional to the difference in their temperatures.
    d.   The quantity of thermal energy exchanged by two bodies in contact is directly proportional to the difference in their temperatures.
    e.   Different amounts of thermal energy are transferred between two bodies in contact if different temperature scales are used to measure the temperature difference between the bodies.

34.   In which process will the internal energy of the system NOT change?

    a.   An adiabatic expansion of an ideal gas.
    b.   An isothermal compression of an ideal gas.
    c.   An isobaric expansion of an ideal gas.
    d.   The freezing of a quantity of liquid at its melting point.
    e.   The evaporation of a quantity of a liquid at its boiling point.

35. For an astronaut working outside a spaceship, the greatest loss of heat would occur by means of

   a. conduction.
   b. convection.
   c. radiation.
   d. conduction and convection.
   e   conduction and radiation.

36. Which statement below regarding the First Law of Thermodynamics is most correct?

   a. A system can do work externally only if its internal energy decreases.
   b. The internal energy of a system that interacts with its environment must change.
   c. No matter what other interactions take place, the internal energy must change if a system undergoes a heat transfer.
   d. The only changes that can occur in the internal energy of a system are those produced by non-mechanical forces.
   e. The internal energy of a system cannot change if the heat transferred to the system is equal to the work done by the system.

37. How much heat, in joules, is required to convert 1.00 kg of ice at 0°C into steam at 100°C? ($L_{ice} = 333\,\mathrm{J/g}$; $L_{steam} = 2.26 \times 10^3\,\mathrm{J/g}$.)

   a. 3.35×10^5
   b. 4.19×10^5
   c. 2.36×10^6
   d. 2.69×10^6
   e. 3.01×10^6

38. Water at room temperature, 20°C, is pumped into a reactor core where it is converted to steam at 200°C. How much heat (in J) is transferred to each kilogram of water in this process? ($c_{steam} = 2010\,\mathrm{J/kg\,°C}$; $L_{steam} = 2.26 \times 10^3\,\mathrm{J/g}$; 1 cal = 4.186 J.)

   a. 3.35×10^5
   b. 7.53×10^5
   c. 2.67×10^6
   d. 2.80×10^6
   e. 3.01×10^6

39. A gas expands from A to B as shown in the graph. Calculate the work (in joules) done by the gas. (1 atm= 1.01×10^5 N/m².)

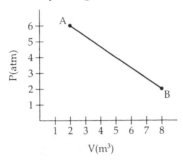

a.   12
b.   24
c. 1.21×10^6
d. 2.42×10^6
e. 3.64×10^6

40. A gas expands as shown in the graph. If the heat taken in during this process is 1.02×10^6 J and 1 atm= 1.01×10^5 N/m², the change in internal energy of the gas (in J) is

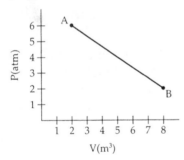

a. -2.42×10^6
b. -1.40×10^6
c. -1.02×10^6
d. 1.02×10^6
e. 1.40×10^6

41. In a thermodynamic process, the internal energy of a system in a container with adiabatic walls decreases by 800 J. Which statement is correct?

a.   The system lost 800 J by heat transfer to its surroundings.
b.   The system gained 800 J by heat transfer from its surroundings.
c.   The system performed 800 J of work on its surroundings.
d.   The surroundings performed 800 J of work on the system.
e.   The 800 J of work done by the system was equal to the 800 J of heat transferred to the system from its surroundings.

42.   If a person in Alaska were locked out of his house on a day when the temperature outside was –40°C, he would be most likely to lose the most thermal energy by

    a.   conduction.
    b.   convection.
    c.   radiation.
    d.   all of the above.
    e.   convection and radiation.

43.   The Earth intercepts 1.27×10^{17} W of radiant energy from the Sun. Suppose the Earth, of volume 1.08×10^{21} m^3, was composed of water. How long would it take for the Earth at 0°C to reach 100°C, if none of the energy was radiated or reflected back out into space?

    a.   26.9 y
    b.   113 y
    c. 2.69×10^4 y
    d. 1.13×10^5 y
    e. 2.69×10^7 y

Open-Ended Problems

44.   100 grams of liquid nitrogen at 77 K is stirred into a beaker containing 200 grams of 5°C water. If the nitrogen leaves the solution as soon as it turns to gas, how much water freezes? (The heat of evaporation of nitrogen is 6.09 cal/gram and the heat of fusion of water is 80 cal/gram.)

45.   How much water at 20°C is needed to melt 1 kilogram of solid mercury at –39°C? (The heat of fusion of mercury is 2.8 cal/gram).

46.   A styrofoam container used as a picnic cooler contains a block of ice at 0°C. If 225 grams of ice melts in 1 hour, how much heat energy per second is passing through the walls of the container? (The heat of fusion of ice is 3.33×10^5 J/kg).

47.   In braking an automobile, the friction between the brake drums and brake shoes converts the car's kinetic energy into heat. If a 1500-kg automobile traveling at 30 m/s brakes to a halt, how much does the temperature rise in each of the four 8-kg brake drums? (The specific heat of each iron brake drum is 448 J/kg °C).

Chapter 20

Heat and the First Law of Thermodynamics

1.	b		25.	c
2.	b		26.	a
3.	c		27.	c
4.	d		28.	b
5.	d		29.	b
6.	e		30.	a
7.	b		31.	d
8.	d		32.	d
9.	a		33.	d
10.	d		34.	b
11.	c		35.	c
12.	b		36.	e
13.	a		37.	e
14.	a		38.	d
15.	d		39.	d
16.	c		40.	b
17.	a		41.	c
18.	d		42.	e
19.	a		43.	d
20.	a		44.	none
21.	b		45.	23.4 grams
22.	c		46.	20.8 J (per second)
23.	d		47.	47°C
24.	a			

Chapter 21

The Kinetic Theory of Gases

Multiple Choice

1. A container having a volume of 1.0 m^3 holds 5.0 moles of helium gas at 50°C. If the helium behaves like an ideal gas, the total energy of the system is

    a. 2.0×10^4 J.
    b. 2.5×10^4 J.
    c. 1.7×10^3 J.
    d. 1.5×10^3 J.
    e. 4.0×10^4 J.

2. A container having a volume of 1.0 m^3 holds 5.0 moles of helium gas at 50°C. If the helium behaves like an ideal gas, the average kinetic energy per molecule is

    a. 6.7×10^{-20} J.
    b. 1.0×10^{-21} J.
    c. 1.0×10^{-20} J.
    d. 6.7×10^{-21} J.
    e. 1.3×10^{-20} J.

3. The average kinetic energy of a nitrogen molecule at room temperature (20°C) is

    a. 2×10^{-21} J.
    b. 4×10^{-21} J.
    c. 6×10^{-21} J.
    d. 8×10^{-21} J.
    e. 1×10^{-20} J.

4. The average translational speed of a nitrogen molecule at room temperature (20°C) is approximately (in m/s)

    a.   100.
    b.   500.
    c.   300.
    d.   700.
    e.   200.

5.   A box contains about 5.0×10^{21} hydrogen atoms at room temperature (21°C). Determine the thermal energy of these atoms.

    a.   10 J
    b.   20 J
    c.   30 J
    d.   5.0 J
    e.   1.0 J

6.   Five gas molecules are found to have speeds of 100, 200, 300, 400, and 500 m/s. The rms speed (in m/s) is

    a.   390.
    b.   300.
    c.   360.
    d.   330.
    e.   320.

7.   Find the specific heat (in cal/mole K) of a gas kept at constant volume when it takes 1.0×10^4 J of heat to raise the temperature of 5.0 moles of the gas 200 K above the initial temperature.

    a.   7.5
    b.   5.0
    c.   2.4
    d.   10
    e.   20

8.   The air in an automobile engine at 20°C is compressed from an initial pressure of 1.0 atm and a volume of 200 cm^3 to a volume of 20 cm^3. Find the temperature if the air behaves like an ideal gas ($\gamma = 1.4$) and the compression is adiabatic.

    a.   730°C
    b.   460°C
    c.   25°C
    d.   50°C
    e.   20°C

9.   During an adiabatic compression, a volume of air decreases to 1/4 its original size. Calculate its final pressure if its original pressure was 1 atm. (Assume the air behaves like an ideal gas with $\gamma = 1.4$.)

    a.   7.0
    b.   5.6
    c.   3.5
    d.   2.2
    e.   0.14

10. An ideal gas is allowed to expand adiabatically until its volume increases by 50%. By approximately what factor is the pressure reduced? ($\gamma = 5/3$.)

    a.   1.5
    b.   2.0
    c.   2.5
    d.   3.0
    e.   3.5

11. When we say that the speed of sound is measured under adiabatic conditions we assume that

    a.   the time associated with heat conduction is slow relative to the speed of the wave.
    b.   no heat can flow between the system and its surroundings.
    c.   the speed of the wave is directly proportional to the bulk modulus.
    d.   the speed of the wave is proportional to the square root of the bulk modulus.
    e.   air is an ideal gas.

12. Assume 3.0 moles of a diatomic gas has an internal energy of 10 kJ. Determine the temperature of the gas after it has reached equilibrium.

    a.   270 K
    b.   160 K
    c.   800 K
    d.   1550 K
    e.   400 K

13. Nitrogen gas is heated by a pulsed laser to 50 000 K. If the diameter of the nitrogen atoms is assumed to be 1.0×10^{-10} m, and the pressure is 1.0 atm, what is the mean free path?

    a. 1.5×10^{-4} m
    b. 1.5×10^{-7} m
    c. 1.5×10^{-10} m
    d. 1.5×10^{-14} m
    e. 1.5×10^{-2} m

14. Assume molecules have an average diameter of 3.00×10^{-10} m. How many times larger is the mean free path than the diameter at STP? (Assume the pressure is 1.01×10^5 N/m^2.)

    a.   500
    b.   300
    c.   700
    d.   1000
    e.   2500

15.   The internal energy of n moles of an ideal gas depends on

   a.   one state variable T.
   b.   two state variables T and V.
   c.   two state vartiables T and P.
   d.   three state variables T, P and V.
   e.   four variables R, T, P and V.

16.   A molecule in a uniform ideal gas can collide with other molecules when their centers are equal to or less than

   a.   one radius away from its center.
   b.   one diameter away from its center.
   c.   two diameters away from its center.
   d.   twice the cube root of volume away from its center.
   e. $\sqrt{2}$ diameters away from its center.

17.   The average molecular translational kinetic energy of a molecule in an ideal gas is

   a. $\dfrac{3}{2}k_\mathrm{B}T$.

   b. $\dfrac{3}{2}RT$.

   c. $\dfrac{5}{2}k_\mathrm{B}T$.

   d. $\dfrac{5}{2}RT$.

   e. $\dfrac{n+3}{2}k_\mathrm{B}T$, where n = number of internal degrees of freedom.

18.   The relation $PV = nRT$ holds for all ideal gases. The additional relation PV^γ holds for an adiabatic process. The figure below shows two curves: one is an adiabat and one is an isotherm. Each starts at the same pressure and volume. Which statement is correct? (Note: "$\propto$" means "is proportional to".)

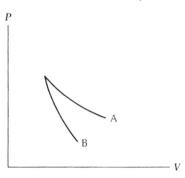

a.   Isotherm: $P \propto \dfrac{1}{V}$; Adiabat: $P \propto \dfrac{1}{V}$: A is both an isotherm and an adiabat.

b.   Isotherm: $P \propto \dfrac{1}{V^\gamma}$; Adiabat: $P \propto \dfrac{1}{V}$: B is an isotherm, A is an adiabat.

c.   Isotherm: $P \propto \dfrac{1}{V}$; Adiabat: $P \propto \dfrac{1}{V^\gamma}$: A is an isotherm, B is an adiabat.

d.   Isotherm: $P \propto \dfrac{1}{V^\gamma}$; Adiabat: $P \propto \dfrac{1}{V^\gamma}$: B is both an isotherm and an adiabat.

e.   I cannot answer this without additional information about the starting temperature.

19.   Which statement below is **NOT** an assumption made in the molecular model of an ideal gas?

a.   The average separation between molecules is large compared with the dimensions of the molecules.
b.   The molecules undergo inelastic collisions with one another.
c.   The forces between molecules are short range.
d.   The molecules obey Newton's laws of motion.
e.   Any molecule can move in any direction with equal probability.

20.   The theorem of equipartition of energy states that the energy each degree of freedom contributes to each molecule in the system (an ideal gas) is

a. $\dfrac{1}{2}mv^2$.

b. $\dfrac{1}{3}k_BT$.

c. $\dfrac{1}{2}k_BT$.

d. $\dfrac{3}{2}mv^2$.

e. $\dfrac{3}{2}k_BT$.

21.   The specific heat at constant volume at 0°C of one mole of an ideal monatomic gas is

    a. $\frac{1}{2}R$.

    b. R.

    c. $\frac{3}{2}R$.

    d. $2R$.

    e. $\frac{5}{2}R$.

22.   The specific heat at constant volume at 0°C of one mole of an ideal diatomic gas is

    a. $\frac{1}{2}R$.

    b. R.

    c. $\frac{3}{2}R$.

    d. $2R$.

    e. $\frac{5}{2}R$.

23.   The specific heat at constant pressure at 0°C of one mole of an ideal monatomic gas is

    a. $\frac{1}{2}R$.

    b. R.

    c. $\frac{3}{2}R$.

    d. $2R$.

    e. $\frac{5}{2}R$.

24.   When we consider a thin horizontal layer of the atmosphere, of thickness dy, of area A, with pressure P on the bottom, with an average mass m per molecule, and n_V molecules per unit volume, the magnitude of the difference of the pressure at the top and bottom of the layer is given by $dP =$

    a. $mgdy$.
    b. $mgn_V dy$.
    c. $mgAdy$.
    d. $mgn_V Ady$.
    e. $mgn_V APdy$.

Open-Ended Problems

25.   A 50-gram sample of dry ice (solid CO_2) is placed in a 4-liter container. The system is sealed and allowed to reach room temperature (20°C). By approximately how much does the pressure inside the container increase when the dry ice turns to gas? (Ignore the initial volume of the sample.)

26.   One mole of helium gas expands adiabatically from 2 atm pressure to 1 atm pressure. If the original temperature of the gas is 20°C, what is the final temperature of the gas? ($\gamma = 1.67$)

27.   Air expands adiabatically (no heat in, no heat out) from $T = 300$ K and $P = 100$ atm to a final pressure of 1 atm. Treat the gas as ideal with $\gamma = 1.4$, and determine the final temperature. Compare your result to the boiling points of nitrogen (77.4 K) and oxygen (90.2 K). Could this method result in the liquification of air?

28.   According to kinetic theory, a typical gas molecule in thermal equilibrium at room temperature has a kinetic energy $K = 6.00 \times 10^{-21}$ J, regardless of mass. Estimate the speed at room temperature of a hydrogen molecule H_2 ($m = 3.34 \times 10^{-27}$ kg) and a xenon atom ($m = 2.00 \times 10^{-25}$ kg). [$k_B = 1.38 \times 10^{-23}$ J/K]

29.   During the volcanic eruption of Mt. Pelee in 1902, an incredibly hot "burning cloud" rolled down the mountain and incinerated the town of Saint-Pierre. From the damage done, the temperature in the cloud was estimated at 700°C. If the air temperature was 20°C and the molecular weight of air is 29 grams, estimate the molecular weight of the gas in the "burning cloud" that made it heavier than the surrounding air. [As a follow-on, estimate the most probable composition of the cloud. Some typical volcanic gases are H_2S, SO_2, H_2SO_4, CO_2, NO]

Chapter 21

The Kinetic Theory of Gases

1.	a		16.	b
2.	d		17.	a
3.	e		18.	c
4.	b		19.	b
5.	c		20.	c
6.	d		21.	c
7.	c		22.	e
8.	b		23.	e
9.	a		24.	b
10.	b		25.	the pressure increases by 7 atm
11.	a		26.	222 K
12.	b		27.	80.5 K, some oxygen would liquify
13.	a			
14.	b		28.	1895 m/s, 245 m/s
15.	a		29.	96, H_2SO_4 (sulfuric acid)

Chapter 22

Heat Engines, Entropy, & the Second Law of Thermodynamics

Multiple Choice

1. A gasoline engine absorbs 2500 J of heat and performs 1000 J of mechanical work in each cycle. The efficiency of the engine is

    a. 80%
    b. 40%
    c. 60%
    d. 20%
    e. 50%

2. A gasoline engine absorbs 2500 J of heat and performs 1000 J of mechanical work in each cycle. The amount of heat expelled in each cycle is

    a. 1000 J
    b. 1500 J
    c. 2000 J
    d. 500 J
    e. 3000 J

3. A heat pump has a coefficient of performance of 4. If the heat pump absorbs 20 cal of heat from the cold outdoors in each cycle, the heat expelled (in cal) to the warm indoors is

    a. 34
    b. 27
    c. 36
    d. 40
    e. 80

4. A refrigerator has a coefficient of performance of 4. If the refrigerator absorbs 30 cal of heat from the cold reservoir in each cycle, the heat expelled (in cal) into the heat reservoir is

    a. 40.5
    b. 37.5
    c. 36.5
    d. 34.5
    e. 22.5

5.   A lawn mower has a 6-horsepower engine (1 HP = 750 W). If the engine has an efficiency of 20%, and the throttle is such that the engine cycles 10 times a second, the heat that is expelled in one cycle is

    a.   1800 J
    b.   2000 J
    c.   2200 J
    d.   2400 J
    e.   2250 J

6.   A steam engine is operating at its theoretical maximum efficiency of 60%. If the waste heat has a temperature of 100°F (38°C), what is the temperature of the boiler?

    a.   350°C
    b.   94°C
    c.   225°C
    d.   504°C
    e.   775°C

7.   A company that produces pulsed gas heaters claims their efficiency is approximately 90%. If an engine operates between 250°C and 25°C, what is its maximum thermodynamic efficiency?

    a.   83%
    b.   65%
    c.   43%
    d.   90%
    e.   56%

8.   A heat engine absorbs 2500 J of heat from a hot reservoir and expels 1000 J to a cold reservoir. When it is run in reverse, with the same reservoirs, the engine pumps 2500 J of heat to the hot reservoir, requiring 1500 J of work to do so. Find the ratio of the work done by the heat engine to the work done by the pump. Is the heat engine reversible?

    a.   1.0 (no)
    b.   1.0 (yes)
    c.   1.5 (yes)
    d.   1.5 (no)
    e.   2.5 (no)

9.   On a cold day, a heat pump absorbs heat from the outside air at 14°F (−10°C) and transfers it into a home at a temperature of 86°F (30°C). Determine the maximum COP of the heat pump.

    a.   0.2
    b.   4.4
    c.   0.5
    d.   7.6
    e.   6.7

10.   A new electric power plant has an efficiency of 42%. For every 100 barrels of oil needed to run the turbine, how many are essentially lost as waste heat (in barrels of oil) to the environment?

a.   21
b.   42
c.   58
d.   10
e.   79

11.   An 800-MW electric power plant has an efficiency of 30%. It loses its waste heat in large cooling towers. Approximately how much waste heat (in MJ) is discharged to the atmosphere per second?

a.   1200
b.   1900
c.   800
d.   560
e.   240

12.   A homeowner has a new oil furnace which has an efficiency of 60%. For every 100 barrels of oil needed to heat his house, how much (in barrels of oil) goes up the chimney as waste heat?

a.   20
b.   60
c.   40
d.   80
e.   10

13.   One kilogram of chilled water at 32°F (0°C) is placed in a freezer which is kept at 0°F (–18°C). Approximately how much electric energy (in kilocalories) is needed to operate the compressor to cool this water to 0°F if the room temperature is maintained at 75°F (24°C)? ($L_{ice} = 3.33 \times 10^5 \dfrac{J}{kg}$; $c_{ice} = 2.09 \times 10^3 \dfrac{J}{kg\ °C}$)

a.   13
b.   1.5
c.   15
d.   16
e.   33

14.   One kilogram of chilled water (0°C) is placed in a freezer which is kept at 0°F (-18°C). Approximately how much electric energy (in kilocalories) is needed just to freeze the water if the room temperature is maintained at 75°F (24°C)? ($L_{ice} = 333\,J/g$; $c_{ice} = 209\,J/g\,°C$.)

a.   11
b.   15
c.   16
d.   13
e.   33

15.   An automobile engine operates with an overall efficiency of 12%. How much energy is delivered as waste heat (in gallons of gasoline) for each 10 gallons of fuel burned?

a.   1.2
b.   8.8
c.   6.5
d.   4.7
e.   7.5

16.   An engine is designed to obtain energy from the temperature gradient of the ocean. What is the thermodynamic efficiency of such an engine if the temperature of the surface of the water is 59°F (15°C) and the temperature well below the surface is 41°F (5°C)?

a.   3.5%
b.   67%
c.   31%
d.   17%
e.   96%

17.   A vessel containing 5.0 kg of water at 10°C is put into a refrigerator. The 1/7 HP motor (1 HP = 746 W) runs for 5.0 minutes to cool the liquid to the refrigerator's low temperature, 0°C. What is the COP of the refrigerator?

a.   5.7
b.   4.6
c.   6.5
d.   7.2
e.   3.6

18.   Exactly 500 grams of ice are melted at a temperature of 32°F. ($L_{ice} = 333\,J/g$.) The change in entropy (in J/K) is

a.   321
b.   146
c.   512
d.   610
e.   5230

19.   When water of mass m and specific heat c is heated from absolute temperature T_1 to absolute temperature T_2, its change in entropy is

    a. $cm \ln(T_2/T_1)$
    b. $cm \, (T_2/T_1)$
    c. $cm \, (T_2 - T_1)/T_1$
    d. $cm \, (T_2 - T_1)/T_2$
    e. $cm \, (T_2 - T_1)/(T_2 + T_1)$

20.   The change in entropy of 1.00 kg of water that is heated from 50°C to 100°C is (in cal/K)

    a.   516
    b.   312
    c.   144
    d.   946
    e.   391

21.   The change in entropy of a mass m of a solid substance which has a latent heat of fusion L and melts at a temperature T is

    a. LT/m
    b. $mL \ln(T)$
    c. mLT
    d. mL/T
    e. L/mT

22.   Since $L_{ice} = 333$ J/g, the change in entropy (in cal/K) when 1.00 kg of ice melts is

    a.   144
    b.   291
    c.   312
    d.   516
    e.   80

23.   If n moles of an ideal gas are compressed isothermally from an initial volume V_1 to a final volume V_2, the change in entropy is

    a. $nR \ln (V_2 / V_1)$
    b. $nRT \ln (V_2/V_1)$
    c. $nk_B \ln (V_2/V_1)$
    d. $n \, C_V \int dT/T$
    e. $n \, C_V/T$

24.   Determine the change in entropy (in J/K) when 5.00 moles of an ideal gas at 0°C
are compressed isothermally from an initial volume of 100 cm^3 to a final volume
of 20 cm^3.

    a.   −191
    b.   −52
    c.   −71
    d.   −67
    e.   −208

25.   An ideal gas is allowed to undergo a free expansion. If its initial volume is V_1 and
its final volume is V_2, the change in entropy is

    a. $nR \ln (V_2 / V_1)$
    b. $nRT \ln (V_2/V_1)$
    c. $nk \ln (V_2/V_1)$
    d.   0
    e. $nR\, V_2/V_1$

26.   Find the change in entropy (in J/K) when 5.00 moles of an ideal gas undergo a
free expansion from an initial volume of 20 cm^3 to a final volume of 100 cm^3.

    a.   71
    b.   52
    c.   67
    d.   191
    e.   208

27.   An ideal gas is allowed to expand adiabatically. Assume the process is reversible.
The change in entropy is

    a.   0
    b. $nR \ln (V_2/V_1)$
    c. $nR \ln (T_2/T_1)$
    d. $kn \ln (V_2/V_1)$
    e. $kn \ln (T_2/T_1)$

28.   Find the change in entropy (in J/K) when 5.00 moles of an ideal monatomic gas
are allowed to expand isobarically from an initial volume of 20 cm^3 to a final
volume of 100 cm^3.

    a.   167
    b.   100
    c.   67
    d.   52
    e.   152

29.   Ten kilograms of water at 0°C is mixed with 10 kg of water at 100°C. The change in entropy (in cal/K) of the system is

   a.   1000
   b.   480
   c.   −720
   d.   240
   e.   −168

30.   A vessel containing 10 kg of water is left out where it evaporates. If the temperature remains constant at 20°C, what is the change in entropy (in kcal/K)? (The latent heat of vaporization at 20°C is 585 cal/g.)

   a.   30
   b.   10
   c.   20
   d.   40
   e.   290

31.   A gasoline engine absorbs 2500 J of heat at 250°C and expels 2000 J at a temperature of 50°C. The change in entropy (in J/K) for the system is

   a.   6.2
   b.   4.7
   c.   1.4
   d.   10.9
   e.   3.2

32.   100 grams of molten lead (600°C) is used to make musket balls. If the lead shot is allowed to cool to room temperature (21°C), what is the change in entropy (in J/K) of the lead? (For the specific heat of molten and solid lead use 1.29 J/g °C; the latent heat of fusion and the melting point of lead are 2.45×10^4 J/kg and 327°C.)

   a.   −140
   b.   −252
   c.   −302
   d.   −429
   e.   −100

33.   The reason that we can calculate the change in entropy of a system is that

   a.   entropy always decreases.
   b.   entropy always increases.
   c.   the entropy of the universe always remains constant.
   d.   it depends only on the properties of the initial and final equilibrium states.
   e.   systems always follow reversible paths.

34.   By operating a reversible heat engine with an ideal gas as the working substance in a Carnot cycle and measuring the ratio Q_c/Q_h, we can calculate

  a. n, the number of moles of the ideal gas.
  b.   the ratio V_c/V_h of the volumes of the ideal gas.
  c.   the ratio P_c/P_h of the pressures of the ideal gas.
  d.   the ratio P_cV_c/P_hV_h of the products of volumes and pressures of the ideal gas.
  e.   the value of Avogadro's number.

35.   Which of the following is an almost reversible process?

  a.   The explosion of hydrogen and oxygen to form water.
  b.   Heat transfer through thick insulation.
  c.   The adiabatic free expansion of a gas.
  d.   A slow isothermal compression of a gas.
  e.   A slow leakage of gas into an empty chamber through a small hole in a membrane.

36.   The change in entropy when 1 kg of ice melts at 0°C is (in J/K)

     $(L_{ice} = 333\,\text{J/g}.)$

  a.   335.
  b.   603.
  c.   1220.
  d.   1310.
  e.   2160.

37.   An ideal heat engine can have an efficiency of 1 if the temperature of the low temperature reservoir is

  a.   0 K.
  b.   0°C.
  c.   0°F.
  d.   0°R.
  e.   the same as the temperature of the heat source.

38.   An adiabatic free expansion of a gas in a thermally isolated container is not reversible because

  a.   work must be done on the gas to return it to its original volume.
  b.   heat must be exchanged with the surroundings to return the gas to its original temperature.
  c.   its internal energy has a greater value after the expanded gas is returned to its original volume and temperature.
  d.   of all of the above.
  e.   of (a) and (b) above only.

39.   A Carnot cycle, operating as a heat engine, consists , in the order given, of

    a.   an isothermal expansion, an isothermal compression, an adiabatic
        expansion and an adiabatic compression.

    b.   an adiabatic expansion, an adiabatic compression, an isothermal expansion
        and an isothermal compression.

    c.   an isothermal expansion, an adiabatic compression, an isothermal
        compression and an adiabatic expansion.

    d.   an adiabatic compression, an isothermal compression, an isothermal
        expansion and an adiabatic expansion.

    e.   an isothermal expansion, an adiabatic expansion, an isothermal
        compression and an adiabatic compression.

40.   All real engines are less efficient than the Carnot engine because

    a.   they do not operate through the Otto cycle.
    b.   they do not operate through a reversible cycle.
    c.   the working substance does not maintain a constant volume through the
        cycle.
    d.   the working substance does not maintain a constant pressure through the
        cycle.
    e.   the working substance does not maintain a constant temperature through
        the cycle.

41.   In an engine operating in the Otto cycle, the final volume of the fuel-air mixture
is one sixth the initial volume. Assume $\gamma = 1.4$. The maximum theoretical
efficiency of this cycle, in per cent, is

    a.   17.
    b.   49.
    c.   51.
    d.   56.
    e.   83.

42.   For a gas of N identical molecules of molecular volume V_m in total volume V at
temperature T, the number of ways of locating the N molecules in the volume is

    a. $\dfrac{V_m}{V}$.

    b. $\dfrac{V}{V_m}$.

    c. $\left(\dfrac{V}{V_m}\right)^T$.

    d. $\left(\dfrac{V}{V_m}\right)^N$.

    e. $\ln\left(\dfrac{V}{V_m}\right)$.

Open-Ended Problems

43.   In a nuclear power plant, the reactor produces 500°C steam that is used to power the steam turbines which generate 1500 MW of electrical power. The cooling tower eliminates the waste heat at 50°C. If the efficiency of the plant were that of a Carnot engine, at what rate would waste heat be vented to the atmosphere?

44.   Every second at Niagara Falls, some 5000 m³ of water falls a distance of 50 m. What is the increase in entropy per second due to the falling water? (Assume a 20°C environment).

45.   One end of a copper rod is in thermal contact with a hot reservoir at $T = 500$ K and the other end is in thermal contact with a cooler reservoir at $T = 300$ K. Find the entropy change of each reservoir, and the total entropy change, when 8000 J of heat energy are conducted from one end of the rod to the other with no change in the temperature distribution in the rod.

Chapter 22

Heat Engines, Entropy, & the Second Law of Thermodynamics

1.	b	24.	d
2.	b	25.	a
3.	b	26.	c
4.	b	27.	a
5.	a	28.	a
6.	d	29.	d
7.	c	30.	c
8.	b	31.	c
9.	d	32.	a
10.	c	33.	d
11.	b	34.	d
12.	c	35.	d
13.	c	36.	c
14.	d	37.	a
15.	b	38.	a
16.	a	39.	e
17.	c	40.	b
18.	d	41.	c
19.	a	42.	d
20.	c	43.	1080 MW
21.	d	44.	8360 kJ/K
22.	b	45.	−16.0 J/K, +26.7 J/K, +10.7 J/K
23.	a		